THE UNIVERSE: PLAN OR ACCIDENT?

THE UNIVERSE:
PLAN OR ACCIDENT?

The Religious Implications of Modern Science

by

ROBERT E. D. CLARK, M.A., Ph.D.

ZONDERVAN PUBLISHING HOUSE
GRAND RAPIDS, MICHIGAN

CONTENTS

CHAPTER   PAGE

      TO THE READER 7

    I. ONE WAY TRAFFIC IN PHYSICS 15

   II. CREATION'S CRITICS 26

  III. WORLDS WITHOUT END 43

  IV. "VARIETIES OF CREATURES . . ." 52

   V. PLANETARY INHABITANTS 61

  VI. A PLANET'S BLUE PRINT 73

 VII. EARTH'S BEGINNINGS 80

VIII. CHEMISTRY OF LIFE 92

  IX. ELEMENTS 105

   X. THE LIVING ORGANISM 119

  XI. NATURE—THE FIRST INVENTOR 141

 XII. DESIGN ARGUMENT—IN HISTORY . . . 152

XIII. MIND IN NATURE——? 163

XIV. DESIGN AND ITS CRITICS 181

 XV. COSMIC MIND 192

XVI. EVIL 200

XVII. TWO PHILOSOPHIES 219

      INDEX OF NAMES 237

      INDEX OF SUBJECTS 239

TO THE READER

SCIENCE speaks with more than one voice to our generation. Some claim that it tells of a universe of law and order in which there is no room for the supernatural or the Divine. Others claim that it provides cogent evidence of the existence of a realm that is spiritual, lying behind the realm of law and matter, but they add that God, not being supernatural, can only manifest Himself through the laws of nature. Others, again, invoke science in support of their belief that God is beyond nature but is able to intervene by miracle as occasion demands. According to some, science tells us that the universe is an accident: the result of a freak "winding up" of a cosmic entropy clock; according to others, science proves that the universe is the result of a cosmic plan.

How does it come about that there is so much divergence of opinion? Why is it that science can be, and often is, interpreted in such different ways?

It is evident that much depends upon our starting-point. Either we may seek to learn from the regularity and uniformity of nature or from those instances in which that uniformity appears to fail; either from the laws of physics, chemistry and biology that we can see in operation around us daily, or from those fundamental but inexplicable features of the universe that have not so far been explained by science. And it is not in the least surprising that, since some people start with the first approach and some with the second, there is no general agreement as to the conclusions that ought to be drawn.

This, in part at least, is the cause of our difficulty. But which approach is right? If we wish to learn from science the answers to philosophical questions, how shall we start? What questions shall we ask?

The answer, it would seem, is this. If we appeal to science at all, we must use her methods—not the methods of our own choosing. Now it is a generally accepted principle in science that it is only through the study of the unusual, the odd and the seemingly inexplicable, that man can be led onwards towards new knowledge.

The scientist whose mind revolves only in the grooves of well recognized theory has little chance of discovering important new principles. An important element in the scientific method is the focusing of attention upon the things that science cannot explain, or has difficulty in explaining. In this way only can it be discovered whether known principles will cover all the facts, or whether new principles remain to be discovered.

It is reasonable to apply the same method if we wish to build a reliable philosophy of nature. If we consider only the recognized laws of science we shall never discover whether they are of universal application—we shall not even discover whether they are the most important factors of which we ought to take cognisance. To reach a sane judgement, we must turn to the odd and the peculiar. We must think about things which, in the light of present scientific knowledge, seem inexplicable. We must ask if they are really inexplicable, or only apparently so. Is it likely that the progress of science will cause them to fall into line? And if not, can the inexplicable facts be explained—explained, not of course, in a fundamental sense, but in the scientific sense of *co-ordinated* or *grouped together*—by a new hypothesis or theory which would make them inexplicable no longer. Finally, if we are able to do so we must *test* our theory—we must see whether it can help us to understand yet other facts, which we have overlooked hitherto, whether it will stimulate our minds to research in new directions and so forth. And, as the past history of science has shown on repeated occasions, it will often happen that the good theory, based upon phenomena that once seemed queer and out of the ordinary, will help us to understand the ordinary and commonplace.

This is the scientific method for the discovery of truth—the method upon which the scientific edifice of our day has been built. And it is also the way of 'common sense'—for though its ideas often originate with the inspired guess, its thought-sequences are those that are always used in establishing evidence in every field. The detective, like the scientist, focuses his attention upon the details that seem queer and inconsistent with the knowledge that he already possesses; like the scientist he frames his theories upon those parts of the picture that at first seem odd and inexplicable; like the scientist again he seeks to discover whether his theories are adequate. The economist, the historian, the archaeologist, the linguist—everyone, in fact, whose business it is to discover facts adopts the same procedure.

So successful has the scientific method been, especially in the domain of science, that it is now almost the fashion to pay it an adoring lip-worship. And of those who do so, would-be philosophers who wish to purge religion and to make it scientific are often loudest in their praises: so loud are they, in fact, that the suspicion: "Methinks, he doth protest too much!" is often unavoidable. Nor is the suspicion unfounded, for when we examine the procedure adopted by these writers, it transpires that, in practice, they utterly and indignantly repudiate that basically important element of scientific procedure which we have mentioned. Instead, they build their supposedly scientific philosophies of nature upon the assumption that it is always safe to use the known as an excuse for denying the relevance or even existence of the unknown.

GOD OF THE GAPS

If we would relate science to philosophy or religious belief, it is argued, we must not seek for the meaning of the abnormal, the extraordinary, or that which does not fall in with our expectations, because, if we do so, science will soon catch up with us. And then what shall we do? Hunt for something else that science cannot explain—and shift from that in turn to something else, and so on endlessly, like a cat chasing its own tail?

This argument is commonly used with reference to God—though it has been used in other directions too, notably in connexion with vitalistic theories in biology. When believers use such argument in order to reach the conclusion that God exists, the God they discover, or think they discover, is disdainfully dismissed as a "God of the gaps"—the "gaps" referred to being gaps in knowledge.

Here in this common argument we discern a disingenuous denial of the scientific method. For the scientist does not think in terms of gaps at all—if he did he would soon lose interest in his science. So-called gaps may, of course, turn out to be gaps and no more than gaps, but if so they lose their interest and are forgotten. The scientist lives in the hope that, on investigation, they will turn out to be gaps pregnant with meaning: he is on the look-out, not for something *negative*, but for something *positive*; something that will show that a new principle is at work in nature; something that will create interest among his fellow scientists.

Comparison with the early days of radioactivity is here peculiarly apt. When Pierre and Madame Curie and, later, Rutherford were seeking to focus scientific attention upon the curious properties of radium, many scientists, among them Armstrong the chemist, argued that radium was a little peculiar, perhaps, but nothing to become excited about. The recognized principles of science, it was argued, would soon explain the few phenomena in connexion with radium that could not yet be explained—if, indeed, there were any of importance. Radium was luminous, it was true, but not as brightly so as some materials: it discharged an electroscope, but so did quinine sulphate. It was foolish to postulate an entirely new principle in science on the basis of a mere gap in our knowledge which would, no doubt, be filled in due course.

Now this is exactly the attitude of many modern writers on science and religion. Nor is the attitude confined to agnostics and atheists; it is to be found, too, among theologians. Both parties insist that philosophical inquiry into the fundamental gaps in scientific knowledge is unjustified. Philosophical inquiry, they say, must be generalized from the laboratory: it must be based upon accepted, provable, findings of science: all else is baseless speculation.

THREE OBJECTIONS

Let us look more closely at this point of view. If you discover a "God of the gaps", we are told, not only will He be doomed to be squeezed out of existence as the gaps close, but even before that happens He will be a mere hypothesis and therefore useless for religion. Imagine the psychological state of the young man who pins his faith on a hypothesis that may lose its usefulness overnight! Moreover, this God—or rather this hypothesis—will be an enemy to science, for the notion that God resides in a gap will encourage religious people to frighten off scientists with notices of "trespassers will be prosecuted". For it is impertinent to investigate God by scientific means. . . . In short, according to the theologians who raise these objections, we must look for God everywhere or nowhere and, according to agnostics and atheists we must look for Him nowhere.

The analogy of radioactivity shows how poor this argument is. Early workers did not accept the mutability of atoms because there was a *gap* in man's knowledge concerning certain rare minerals. The evidence was *positive*, not negative. There was definite concrete evidence—it was found, of course, in one of the "gaps" in contemporary science (where else could it be found?)—that supposedly changeless elements did in fact change.

Reconstruct, in imagination, the suggestive ideas prevalent around the turn of the century. Vast supplies of energy from sun and stars—a hint from Lord Kelvin that just possibly an unknown source of energy exists—known changes liberate little energy—mysterious rays from a few rare minerals—these minerals must have emitted their rays for millions of years—little known about them—perhaps connected with energy supplies of universe—widespread philosophical belief that matter contains a gigantic hidden store of energy, etc. The cues that led to the new knowledge were found in gaps. The new energy source was an "energy of the gaps" but none the worse for that.

No reasonable person is interested in gaps for their own sake. Christians of a former generation are sometimes ridiculed today for their outmoded belief in the "God of the gaps", but did they, in fact, even in their wilder moments, ever *really* argue that whatever could not be explained by science was due to God? One may doubt it. Mankind has known for thousands of years that lime gets hot with water (St. Augustine mentions the fact) and that metals change their colours in sulphide solutions, but not till recent times did anyone know why. It was never argued that these gaps in knowledge were a proof that God was performing miracles! Christians in the nineteenth century had not the slightest idea why a strange red spot appeared on Jupiter in 1878 or why there was sometimes a green flash when the sun was setting over the ocean, but they did not account for these rare events in terms of Divine intervention. Mere lack of understanding is not and never has been a reason for seeking a theological explanation. The "God of the gaps" is a modern myth.[1] Christians have often supposed that

[1] Newton supposed that his theory of gravitation was inadequate to explain all the features of the solar system and that some of these features were supplied by "a divine arm". Later, La Place argued that the hypothesis of God was unnecessary. This is often cited as evidence that Newton believed in a "God of the gaps". But the fairness of this judgement is open to doubt. Newton found evidence for God in the *plan* of nature, not in mere gaps in scientific knowledge. He saw in God

they had *positive* evidence for belief in God, and they have sometimes found (or thought they found) the evidence in "gaps". But
again, where else could they have found it? In like manner the
Becquerels, Curies, Rutherfords and Soddys of half a century ago
looked for *positive* evidence of the existence of a new kind of
energy. It was not gaps in knowledge *per se* which interested them.
They did not point to Jupiter's spot or the green flash.

A second objection is this. It is claimed that if, in delving into
the "gaps" of science, we discover (or think we discover) God, we
shall at once become opponents of science. Thereafter, we shall
feel obliged to hinder the scientist at his work, preventing him
from using his tools in the domain of religion—or even of science.

Once again the argument is fallacious. No one deigns to show
how this works out in practice. Let us consider two examples. A
former generation was greatly impressed by the properties of water.
It was generally believed that in this wonderful material mankind
could see very real evidence of the handiwork of God. According
to the modern argument, then, we might have expected bishops to
preach sermons against irreligious scientists who investigated or
"explained" the properties of water. When the Braggs accounted
for the low density of ice (a property that keeps much life alive
through cold winters) we almost begin to wonder if Christians
organized a raid to smash the X-ray apparatus employed! But is
there the slightest evidence of such an attitude? Or again, take the
familiar Bible miracle of the fall of Jericho. Archaeologists have
suggested that an earthquake helped the Israelites. Since when
have Christians opposed archaeology in Palestine on this score?

But what of the claim that a God, reached through science, is a
hypothesis only, and so unworthy of man's adoration and worship?
Here again, the objection is muddled and fallacious. Suffice it to
say that *hypothesis*, in science, has two meanings which are often
confused. No one who has read scientific biographies can be
ignorant of the fact that radically new scientific ideas come as a
result of a faith that is closely allied to religious faith.[1] For the

---

[1] For a development of this theme see R. E. D. Clark, *Christian Belief and Science*:
A Reconciliation and a Partnership (Eng. Univ. Press), 1960.

---

transcendent the Great Engineer, though with Henry More and others he sometimes wondered wistfully whether God *immanent* might not be revealing himself in
gravity, centrifugal force and the like. See I. Hartill, *Jour. Trans. Victoria Inst.*,
1946, **78**, 75.

discoverer, hypothesis and faith may be almost synonymous. Yet in later developments, in working out the details of great ideas, hypothesis stands only for the almost trivial suggestion which can be adopted one day and forgotten the next. A philosophical hypothesis founded on science would be emotionally valueless, were it like the latter, but of deep religious value were it of the former kind.

It seems clear that we must reject, out of hand, the modern myth that investigation of the gaps of science leads, only, to a futile god-of-the-gaps kind of religion. As well might the opponents of the Curies and the Rutherfords have talked derisively of a "radioactivity of the gaps". The unprejudiced man will not limit his horizon before he starts his exploration. Since gaps in knowledge are the fountain of new knowledge, we must boldly explore the supposed gaps with all the care that we can muster. Nor need we apologize for doing so.

THE QUEST

That is the object of this book. In the light of the scientific knowledge of our day we shall seek to explore some of the nooks and crannies of our universe—some of the exceptional features which seem odd, queer and suggestive. We shall try to discover whether it is likely that they really are mere gaps in our knowledge or whether, on the other hand, they can provide us with positive evidence of the operation of principles which remain unrecognized by the materialistic philosophers of our age. And if so—what are those principles? Can they help us to understand the ordinary as well as the odd? Can they help us to construct a philosophy of nature which will end the age-long strife between religion and science?

It is a fascinating quest on which we are about to embark. Men are waiting—longing—for a philosophy that makes sense of the world in which we live; a philosophy which makes sense of the emotional side of man's nature as well as of the facts he knows about the material world. Can the scientific method help in this quest? Can it, if used fairly—not with the mere lip-service that has so often brought its application into disrepute—provide us with such a philosophy?

To the devout religious person the question may seem unimportant. He believes because he has faith, and science will neither strengthen nor diminish that faith. But some of us were born to be doubting Thomases. For us, the quest is profoundly important and every step in its pursuit exciting. Reason may or may not be the only way of discovering truth but it is certainly the only way that doubting Thomas knows. Used fairly and remorselessly—where will reason bring us in the end?

Let us start at the beginning with the creation of the universe.

CHAPTER I

ONE WAY TRAFFIC IN PHYSICS

WAS the universe created or has it existed for ever?
On this, as on so many other subjects, there have been differences of opinion since the dawn of history. Many primitive peoples possess legends telling of a "creation" of one kind or another. According to most of these, a formless waste is supposed to have become ordered into earth, sky and sea by one or other of the various pagan gods and goddesses. Nevertheless, the idea of creation in its strict sense—creation out of nothing, rather than the ordering of pre-existing stuff—appears to occur only in the Hebrew Scriptures.

Among the ancient Greek philosophers some believed in a creation though it was often attributed, not to God, but to an inferior *demiurgos,* a kind of slave god, who did the manual labour in the celestial realms.[1] It is conjectured that this curious idea is connected with the fact that Greek philosophers, who were waited on hand and foot by their slaves, tended to despise work in all its forms.

ETERNAL CYCLES

In the end, however, the best Greek thought settled down to the idea that the universe involves an eternal cycle of events. Just as men and animals start young, grow to maturity, and pass on through senility to death and decay, so the worlds also—for it was believed that there were many worlds beside our own—passed through the same stages. And just as the coming of each new generation seemed like the revival from death of the one that had gone before, so the world revived and started merrily on its way again, a process that continued uninterruptedly from one eternity to the next.

To us this doctrine sounds mechanical and materialistic. Not so

[1] See, for example, F. Solmsen, *Plato's Theology,* 1942, Chap. VI.

to the Greeks. For them, Fate and Providence ruled the world and were possessed, at the least, of a kind of quasi-intelligence.

In the age-long cycles events repeated themselves. Endlessly. Exactly. Freemen and slaves came and went like puppets on the stage, as they had always done, only to come and go once more, when the show was repeated in the aeons that were to follow. Inquisitive Greeks tried to estimate the period that must elapse between one cycle and the next. Some put the figure at 48,000 years.

The cycles were no automatic affair like the winding and re-winding of the hairspring of a watch. In each aeon events were left very much to themselves until the world had, so to speak, unwound and could endure no longer. Then God, or the gods, or the demiurge, stepped in and restored all things as they were at the beginning of the cycle. There was a new golden age and everything began again.

So persuasively were these views promulgated that, even after the lapse of a millennium and a half, they exercised a profound influence upon the thought of the Middle Ages. In the twelfth century A.D., as a result of the discovery of the classical writings and the revival of learning, the intellectuals of the day began to feel that the Hebrew-Christian doctrine of the creation was inconsistent with reason.

Aquinas, perhaps the greatest intellect of his time, felt this difficulty strongly. Although, with skill and enormous persever-ence, he had weaved the newly discovered classical knowledge into a harmonious whole and had convinced his contemporaries that it was compatible with Christianity, yet on this matter he was forced to conclude that it was impossible for the human intellect to discover that the world had been created. A knowledge of the creation could come by faith alone.[1]

EVENTS IN REVERSE

Developments of science in the sixteenth and seventeenth century soon pointed the way to a purely intellectual argument for an original creation of the universe.

Hitherto, scientists had failed to distinguish clearly between two kinds of processes that take place in nature—the reversible and the

[1] E. T. Whittaker, *Space and Spirit*, 1946.

irreversible. The reason for their failure probably lay in the fact that the ancients had been preoccupied with mathematics to the exclusion of physics, while their only developed observational science was that of astronomy. Now the astronomer, gazing at the heavens and seeking to formulate the laws that govern the movements of the stars, sees only a repetition of events. True, an occasional comet, eclipse or new star may seem to violate the rule of uniformity. Yet, even the earliest known astronomers had discovered that the most unusual heavenly events were sometimes predictable. And they would have noticed nothing strange if those events had taken place in reverse—forwards or backwards they would have appeared identical to the eye. In the same way, there was nothing in the laws of motion which, applied to a planet gyrating round a star, would not have made equally good sense if the planet had moved backwards—that is to say if it had moved round the star in the reverse direction.

It must always have been obvious that many events of everyday life, eating for instance, would have looked decidedly queer if they could have been imagined to take place in reverse! Even the ancients were well aware of this fact. Thus, the Romans made lists of impossible events (*adynata*), showing that they recognized, as do we, the existence of natural law in nature. Thus, they instanced the facts that no one can alter the past, that night always follows day, and, significantly, that rivers never flow upstream.[1]

HEAT

The most commonly experienced of all irreversible physical processes are found in connexion with heat. Hot water and cold water mix together to give warm water, but we never find warm water separating itself into its hot and cold constituents. Again, hot bodies heat cold bodies, but we never find the reverse of this process taking place—we do not find cold bodies heating hot ones.

In the later Middle Ages, the nature and behaviour of heat occasioned a great deal of interest. Yet the striking fact that the passage of heat from one body to another affords a beautiful

---

[1] R. M. Grant, *Miracle and Natural Law in Graeco-Roman and Early Christian Thought,* Amsterdam, 1952, p. 57. In early days, however, the expression "natural law" had a moral, not a physical, meaning.

example of an irreversible event of a purely physical kind, does not appear to have struck anyone before the seventeenth century.

Why was this? Probably it was for the following reason. In the middle ages scholars supposed that heat could sometimes create cold and cold, heat. It was claimed, for instance, that ice was sometimes colder than the air that froze it. Again, it was said that the cold air of winter actually made the body hotter than did the heat of summer. Another common argument was that although hail consisted of particles of ice, and would therefore be expected to occur most frequently in winter, yet actually it was much more common in the summer when the air was warm. In the same way hot water, left out on a frosty night, froze more quickly than cold water. Had the schoolmen been familiar with the domestic refrigerator they would have found in it, perhaps, the best argument of all for their view that an abundance of heat could, as it were, concentrate cold and so produce ice and snow. This strange theory, which may be found in the writings of Aristotle, was enthusiastically accepted in medieval times and was known by the name of *antiperistalsis*.

It is interesting to note in passing that when the great fifteenth-century Italian physicist, Giovanni Marliani, was a boy of thirteen, he was firmly convinced that antiperistalsis was nonsense—which, indeed, it is. But when he grew older, he succumbed to the authority of Aristotle and to that of the learned men of his day with whom he vied in spinning theories to account for it.[1] A better commentary on the text to the effect that God sometimes hides the truth from the wise and prudent but reveals it to babes can scarcely be conceived.

The theory of antiperistalsis made it impossible for the philosophers and scientists of the Middle Ages to recognize irreversibility in the behaviour of heat. Not until Aristotle had been discredited —chiefly as a result of the Reformation—and scientists had begun to study nature anew with unprejudiced minds, did that appear obvious which had been so clearly recognized by a thirteen-year-old boy in the fifteenth century.

It is likely enough that an extended study of the scientific writings of the sixteenth and seventeenth centuries would reveal many instances in which the irreversible nature of the laws of heat were recognized. No study from this point of view appears, how-

[1] M. Glagett. *Giovanni Marliani and Late Medieval Physics*, 1941.

ever, to have been undertaken. It is sufficient to note that a recognition of the idea is to be found quite clearly expressed in the writings of Newton.

NEWTON'S ARGUMENT

In his well-known *Letters to Bentley*,[1] Newton points out that hot objects always warm cold ones until the two are at the same temperature. But the universe, he says, contains hot and cold bodies which have not, apparently, had time to reach thermal equilibrium. It follows that such a state of affairs cannot have existed for ever. It was quite impossible, too, to suppose that a primordial gas, condensing as a result of gravitational forces, could have produced both cold and hot bodies. The universe could not, therefore, be explained on materialistic lines but must have been made by God.

Thus a recognition of the fact that some events take place in one direction only, so that a reversal of them becomes unthinkable, led Newton at once to see that science afforded evidence of an original creation. (For the moment we need not pause to consider the precise meaning of the word *creation*. We shall discuss this point in the sequel. Any who are disposed to be impatient at this procedure are asked to remember that even the writer of a dictionary must use words before he has explained their meanings!)

HEAT AND ENTROPY

It appears that Newton's argument was, in time, forgotten. Nor is this surprising for, in the eighteenth century, science took a wrong turn and progress was greatly slowed down. Not until recent times was attention again directed to Newton's argument and even then this only took place in a roundabout way as a result of the study of the physics of the steam-engine.

For a long time the knowledge that energy reveals itself, now in one form and now in another, remained hidden. This was doubtless because, by our standards, a very great deal of energy is equivalent to only a little heat. As a result, the fact that mechanical work can always be converted into heat—as for instance when blocks of ice are rubbed together—was for long overlooked. The

[1] A summary of these letters will be found in Brewster's *Life of Newton* (Vol. II, p. 125 ff.).

true interpretation *had* been discovered by Robert Hooke in the seventeenth century but later, in the eighteenth, heat came to be regarded as a special kind of substance (called *caloric*), and it was not until well into the nineteenth century that its true nature was again recognized.

With the coming of industry, with its enormous demand for power, it became a matter of prime importance to discover the best ways of turning heat into work. Calculations showed that the process had hitherto been inefficient in the extreme. It was easy to turn the *whole* of mechanical work into heat, but only a small fraction of the heat could be turned back into work. What was the reason for this? Was it possible to manufacture engines which would produce five or ten times the power for the same consumption of coal?

This is no place to discuss the work of those scientists who sought to answer these questions. Suffice it to say that it soon became a very important matter for the engineer to be able to calculate quickly how much energy he could get out of his steam. It was found that the use of a certain mathematical expression, depending both upon the quantity of heat in a pound of steam and also upon its temperature, made the calculation easy.

Many mathematical expressions used by engineers and scientists stand for an obvious property of a material and mean something to the layman. Occasionally, however, this is not so and it is then that their inventors are often driven, perforce, to invent fancy names. The expression we have been speaking about in the last paragraph is one of this kind and it came to be called *entropy,* and was given the symbol S. Soon the engineering handbooks contained pages of tabulated values of entropy for steam under different conditions, but entropy at first attracted little attention outside the world of engineering. However, it was soon realized that it possessed the remarkable property of increasing in physical changes and it was possible to prove that, were it ever to do otherwise, perpetual motion machines would be possible.

The rule that entropy increases came to be known as the *law of entropy* or the *second law of thermodynamics.* There are a number of other ways of expressing the law all of which come to the same thing. Several physicists pointed out that since the rather meaningless *entropy* increased in every physical change, it ought therefore to be increasing for the entire universe, but no one knew whether this was important.

Under the influence of this purely mechanical idea, the science and technology of heat increased by leaps and bounds. Engine efficiencies, higher than hitherto reached, were attained. Vast sums of money were saved from being wasted on machines (e.g. those which used ether and other liquids in place of water in the ordinary steam-engine) which would never have worked efficiently.

In time the entropy law brought to light many other hitherto unknown laws of science which, in turn, led to great advances in the physical and chemical sciences. In short, it soon became apparent that the entropy law—the rule that the mysterious S must always increase—was one of the most remarkable and far reaching generalizations that have ever been formulated by the human mind. But still the nature of entropy remained an unsolved puzzle.

Eventually, the mystery was solved by Boltzmann. His treatment was mathematical but the fundamental ideas upon which it was based can be explained easily enough without flights into technicalities.

ORDER AND DISORDER

We have mentioned the fact, recognized by the ancients, that some natural processes only proceed in one direction whereas others seem able to take place either forwards or backwards. Clearly, there must be a difference between natural events of the two kinds.

What, then, is the difference? To clear our minds let us suppose that photographic "shots" are taken of various everyday events and that the films, after processing, are shown on the screen both forwards and backwards. The passing landscape photographed from the window of a train, the swinging pendulum bob or the gyrations of a model of the moon or of a planet all make sense, independently of which way they are shown.[1] But imagine films of another kind

---

[1] H. Dingle has, on several occasions (*Through Science to Philosophy*, 1937, etc.) stressed the point that this is not *strictly* true. Thus, if we watch a pendulum bob or a satellite long enough, we shall observe that something irreversible is superimposed on the obvious reversible events—the motion of the pendulum dies down while the satellite may approach its planet and eventually burn up. However, this point in no way affects the conclusions reached in this chapter, though it is possible, as Dingle points out, so to frame the laws of mechanics that the irreversible nature of all events becomes more obvious—a fact which did not elude Newton's eagle eye: "Motion is much more apt to be lost than got, and is always upon the decay" (J. W. N. Sullivan. *Isaac Newton*, 1938, p. 105).

—a man eating a fish, a gun being fired, a bomb hitting a house, a coal fire burning, a blast furnace at work, or even the proverbial Humpty Dumpty falling from the wall—and in each instance there is clearly something bizarre and nonsensical about the film when it is shown backwards. It is against all our experience of nature to suppose that any of this class of events can ever take place in reverse!

In what way do these two classes of events—the reversible and the irreversible—differ from one another? The answer is obvious. When elaborately organized structures become disarranged the process is irreversible:

> All the King's horses and all the King's men
> Could not put Humpty Dumpty together again.

On the other hand, when order is not destroyed, we find that nature can carry out her processes equally well in either direction.

Now heat is, apparently, an exception to this rule. It is not immediately obvious that arrangement or order is destroyed when hot and cold water are mixed. Nevertheless, even heat often conforms readily enough to the traditional Humpty Dumpty pattern. The burning of a log of wood, or of a cigar, are events not so very different in kind from an egg falling off a wall.

Now Boltzmann made the suggestion that *all* irreversible processes involving heat really involve the disordering of molecules. He claimed, in short, that atoms and molecules are so exceedingly small and are present in such countless millions in every piece of visible matter, that any order they possess as a whole will be incapable of appealing to our senses. Nevertheless, when hot and cold water are mixed, what is really happening is that the invisible order is being dissipated. Starting with this point of view, he was able to prove that the mathematical expression which the engineers were in the habit of using in order to measure entropy, was really a measure of the disorder in a system. And in some instances he was able to calculate entropy accurately from a knowledge of the numbers and positions of atoms.

In what way can hot or cold water possess an organization which becomes disorganized when they are mixed?

We can answer this question by imagining a simple model. A

group of balls lies motionless on a billiard table. Another group of balls is cannoned into their midst. After the inevitable impacts, all the balls are moving but the original state of affairs—half the balls still and the other half moving—is never restored again. During the collisions something irreversible has happened.

This simple mechanical picture suggests that something similar will happen with heat also. For we may compare the still and moving balls to the molecules in cold and hot water. And just as the balls, after becoming mingled, never restore themselves to their first state, so lukewarm water never separates out into the hot and cold water from which it may have been prepared.

So we see that the irreversible process which takes place between hot and cold bodies is no exception to the general rule of nature—the rule that all events which involve the disappearance of order are irreversible, while those that do not, are potentially, at least, reversible. (Actually, this statement needs to be qualified slightly—for "all events" we should have said "all events involving more than a few molecules"—but this is of no consequence at present.)

The order present in hot and cold water before they are mixed is, of course, of a rather peculiar kind, but it is order, nevertheless. It is just as real as the order in the arrangement of the words of a book, or the order in the dabs of paint on the canvas of a portrait. It is as difficult to conceive of chance providing all the molecules in one bucket of water with a disproportionate share of energy compared with those in another bucket, as it is to suppose that chance would arrange the words in a book or the paint of a portrait.

Thus the famous law of entropy simply amounts to this—that every ordered arrangement tends to become disordered.[1] In every-day life, disordering may or may not take place. The printed words in a book do not change places and cease to make sense after the lapse of a few centuries, neither does our crockery break unless we drop it on the floor. Some forms of order are stable and can only be destroyed with difficulty. But in the realm of the atoms and molecules such stability is more rare. In gases and liquids there is

[1] Strictly speaking the law of entropy is a *particular example* of the more general law (the *law of morpholysis*) that disorder increases. The latter has also been expressed in the statement that asymmetry disappears and is replaced by symmetry—a formulation due, chiefly, to Pierre Curie (1884). Whyte calls this "the Unitary Principle". See L. L. Whyte, *The Unitary Principle in Physics and Biology*, 1949.

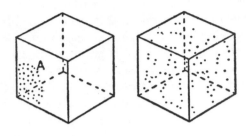

FIG. I.

Diagram showing the simplest possible instance of
spontaneous disordering. A group of molecules placed
in a corner of a box, as at A, rapidly and spontaneously
fills the box, the process being irreversible.

(*Courtesy John Murray*)

never-ceasing turmoil—the particles are constantly striking one
another and rebounding. No wonder, then, if order stored in
molecular assemblages steadily disappears. With solids, however,
there is more stability. Nevertheless, in all states of matter and at
all levels of size, disorder naturally tends to increase or else, if it is
prevented from doing so, its quantity remains unchanged. In no
instance does it diminish: order can always disappear into nowhere
but it cannot come from nowhere.

ENTROPY AND GOD

Now the startling thing about nature is that the energy of the
universe still possesses order, despite the fact that that order is
constantly decreasing. On every hand we see evidences of this fact.
Intense heat and intense cold, flaming suns and planets covered
with liquefied gases, show how unequally the different atoms have
been endowed with energy.[1]

Thus the evidence of science is to the effect that the entropy (or
disorder in the distribution of energy) of the universe is increasing
towards a maximum.

Although put in modern terms, and although today precise
measurements of entropy have become possible, this generalization
is the same in principle as that made by Sir Isaac Newton, which
we mentioned at the beginning of this chapter. Thus, the physics

[1] This fact is in no way altered by the consideration that mass and energy are
interchangeable.

of the steam-engine has led to the recognition of one of the most important of all physical laws, one that was known in principle centuries ago, and was always recognized by common sense, but one which did not take its rightful place in science until the modern era.

But Newton went further. He claimed that the entropy law (though he did not call it by that name) was an argument for believing that in a distant past God had created the world. Was he right in this conjecture?

We may attempt to put Newton's argument in modern dress. Let us imagine a discarnate being (popularly known as a "Maxwellian demon"—though the idea originated with Lord Kelvin) who can "see" molecules. Let us also suppose that he is able to manipulate a trap door which separates two halves of a box. (The manipulation of a trap-door need, in principle, involve no expenditure of energy, though it is implied that small quantities of energy must be stored.) Let us now suppose that when he sees fast molecules coming, he allows them to pass his trap-door, but that he refuses entry to the slow ones. In this way, after a while, he can separate a gas of uniform temperature into a hot half and a cold half. Maxwell suggested that mind, and mind alone, could, therefore, defeat the entropy law by acting intelligently upon its surroundings.

The argument has been criticized in recent years. It can be shown that if the discarnate being employs light to "see" the molecules, he will create entropy by so doing, in amount greater than or equal to that which he destroys in his box. (This happens because quanta of light, by bouncing from the molecules, cause them to move erratically.) However, this criticism seems to beg the question—it merely shows that *if* the discarnate mind operates *as a purely physical mechanism*—then it will do what all physical mechanisms must inevitably do—produce overall disorder. But a being who knew, by psychical power and without physical aid, the positions and speeds of molecules, would, *in principle,* be able to diminish entropy or create order.

Obviously no one supposes that God depends upon physical mechanisms for his knowledge. *In principle,* therefore, Newton's suggestion seems reasonable.

CHAPTER II

CREATION'S CRITICS

WHAT are we to conclude about the "entropy" argument for an original creation? Certainly, there are many who refuse to take it seriously and their number has, perhaps, increased in recent years.

First of all there is the criticism of the intelligent non-scientific man who feels certain that there is a "snag" somewhere in the entropy law. "Surely," he will say, "there must be a fallacy in a law which states that things cannot order themselves. Do we not see order arising every day of our lives? Clouds make patterns in the sky; snowflakes are beautifully and artistically designed; crystals of exquisite shapes are formed in liquids; the sea leaves ripples on the sand as the tide goes down. In view of these and many other instances, it is surely hard to believe that disorder is always increasing or that order never comes into existence of its own accord!"

This argument is the same, in principle, as the old idea of antiperistalsis which for so many years prevented the recognition of the entropy law. It is true that the order associated with energy is running down—that energy is constantly becoming more evenly distributed. Nevertheless it is possible to build refrigerators and heat pumps that make cold from heat or heat from cold. The process is wasteful and, considered in totality, energy is dissipated as anyone can confirm who opens the doors of a refrigerator to keep the kitchen cool on a hot summer's day!

The examples cited all illustrate the same point. When a substance crystallizes or when a snowflake forms in the sky, potential energy stored in a physical or chemical form is dissipated as highly disordered heat. But some of the original order may be preserved in the process and may appear in the crystal, despite the fact that, taken as a whole, the process results in a loss of order. If cloud patterns form in the sky they do so only as a side-show in the general dissipation of energy. The scientific investigation of these and all similar phenomena aims at understanding the mechanism by which a certain amount of order is salved while the larger part is dissipated.

AN ANALOGY

An entertaining analogy[1] shows how this can come about. Imagine small insects which hop—fleas will do—enclosed in a box with two sections A and B (Fig. 2a). We place the insects in A but as a result of their continual hopping they become divided equally between A and

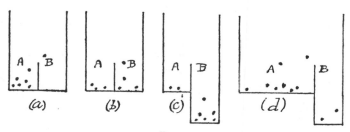

FIG. 2.

B (as in Fig. 2b). Now suppose that B is made lower than A. A new equilibrium is established and B now contains more insects than A, as in c. The change takes place in such a direction that energy is dissipated—it would, in fact, be possible to obtain a little useful energy by making the fleas jump upon a small Pelton wheel placed in B. If, however, no attempt is made to collect the energy, the fleas in B will be slightly "warmer" (more energetic) than those in A. This extra heat will be lost to the surroundings of the box. The heat liberated will exactly correspond to the loss of potential energy.

Now imagine the compartment A to be increased in area, as in d. Many of the fleas will now collect in A once more. This happens because a flea, once it has jumped in B, has a good chance of returning to A, because A is large. But, if it hops in A, it will often fall back into the same compartment once more. Energy will be gained in passing from B to A and this energy can only come from heat, with the result that the fleas will become "cooler" (less energetic) in the process.

There are, then, two factors which help fleas to leave a given compartment—they will be encouraged to leave if, (1) they lose potential energy by so doing, or (2), if a change of habitat will enable them to live in a more scattered state, i.e. if their *entropy* rises.

Water finds its own level and, if we put a little water in our box, it will all collect in B, at the lowest possible level. But when constant

[1] Due to H. F. Blum, *Time's Arrow and Evolution*, Princeton, 1951. (Adapted)

movement—the hopping insects or the ceaseless agitation of matter due to heat (Brownian movement)—enters the picture, then increase in entropy becomes balanced against loss in potential energy. This means that events can occur in such a way that heat is lost—as when we dissolve salts in water and observe a fall in temperature at the expense of breaking up a crystalline structure and leaving the molecules in a more scattered state. In like manner, we may lower B yet further, when insects will leave A and again enter B, where they may become trapped if they cannot hop high enough to escape. When this happens order is created and entropy falls, but only at the expense of a loss in potential energy. The fleas, once widely separated, are now in close contact and, transferring our thoughts again to molecules, we can understand why the pressure forces them to take up a crystalline form—for marbles or needles shaken up in a box arrange themselves in just those ways that cause least obstruction to their neighbours.

The law of entropy not only predicts that in Fig. 2d fleas will hop *upwards* from B to A, but also that in c they will hop *downwards* from A to B. For when potential energy is lost, disorder is created. To illustrate—imagine a million drops of water falling over a cataract. One and all they describe smooth curves over the edge and down into the abyss. At the bottom there is an inferno of disorder and, as it settles down, the water gets warmer. Potential energy has been dissipated— the process cannot be reversed. Loss of potential energy, equally with loss of order of concentration (as with the fleas), or of position of particles (as in crystals) or any other kind of loss of order is all the same to nature. Loss in one may be partly balanced by gain elsewhere— but, overall, the entropy law is, apparently, the most fundamental of all the laws we know. Even the apparently exceptions to it have provided the strongest evidence of its truth. Exception has proved the rule.

Only when we come to deal with a very *few* particles, or molecules— or with a slightly larger number and very long aeons of time—may we expect rather trivial exceptions. It is not difficult for three balls on a golf course to arrange themselves in line by chance, but not a thousand, and certainly not a quadrillion (10^{24}—roughly the number of molecules in a handful of matter). It would happen very infrequently with four, but if golf enthusiasts knocked balls around for hundreds of years it might happen once in a while even with five or six. But spontaneous ordering of this kind is a far cry from the numbers with which we have to deal in nature.

INFINITE UNIVERSE

There are, however, many who claim that the entropy law, though true, cannot be used fairly as evidence of an original creation. The arguments used fall into three classes.

In the first place, it has been stated again and again—one writer copying from another, as is usual on such matters—that although the entropy law holds in all *finite* systems, we must not jump to the conclusion that it also holds for an *infinite* universe. Another way of putting the same argument is to say that although the law holds for all the *parts* we must not apply it to the *whole*. Reasons for this statement are not generally forthcoming except that we are told to be wary of dangerous extrapolations. One writer,[1] however, says that if we apply the law to the *whole* of the universe, we shall have no objective standard with which to "test the alleged increase" in entropy. This is possibly true, but seems to show some confusion of thought. The fact that we cannot test (or measure) the increase for the entire universe can hardly prevent such an increase taking place!

The fear that if the entropy argument is applied to the universe at large, it will inevitably mean that sooner or later God will have to be introduced, leads rationalists to a curiously obscurantist position. Thus Joseph McCabe writes: "To deny that there is, in the obscure depths of space, a compensating or restoring mechanism is an unscientific and illogical piece of dogmatism. There is no use appealing to thermodynamic laws. They express our experience, not what lies beyond our experience."[2]

Similarly J. Needham remarks that "the ever-present possibility of cyclical trends . . . or a continuous flow of energy through the universe" make deductions from the entropy law unconvincing.[3]

Comment hardly seems necessary. Eddington well remarked that when a physicist writes about the heat-death of the universe,

[1] E. A. Milne, *Manchester Literary and Philosophical Society, Memoirs*, 1933–4, Vol. 78, p. 9 ff.

[2] *The Riddle of the Universe Today*, 1934, p. 202. This quotation is reminiscent of an argument in Bertrand Russell's *Why I am Not a Christian* (1927, p. 18). In discussing the problem of evil, Russell compares the universe to a crate of oranges in which all the top ones are bad and he concludes that the rest must be bad also. But he complains that Christians argue: "The underneath ones must be good so as to redress the balance"!

[3] *History is on Our Side*, 1946, p. 212.

critics complain that it is most unsafe to extrapolate from our limited experience of nature. But the self-same critics, in refereeing a paper on, let us say, the possible origin of cosmic rays in galaxies beyond the range of telescopes, would look first of all to see whether the paper was consistent with the second law, and would advise its rejection if this did not prove to be the case.[1]

The argument that the entropy law may be applied to parts of the universe but not to the whole, is easy to refute—whether that whole be finite or infinite.[2] Indeed, it seems fairly clear that this objection is an attempt to befog the issue.

But can we be sure that the entropy law will apply to *every* one of the possible models of the universe that cosmologists have suggested, or *may* suggest in years to come? What about the claim, sometimes made by mathematicians (though other mathematicians obtain the opposite result) that the entropy principle does not apply to a relativistic expanding universe? How can the non-specialist afford to be dogmatic on such matters? How can he even be sure that entropy is not a human artefact?[3]

---

[1] A. S. Eddington, *The Philosophy of Physical Science*, 1939, p. 54.

[2] Let us imagine space to be divided up into a number of zones—say, cubical in shape and of side r. Then all the radiation, gravitational force, etc., which passes from one zone to another must pass through the *surface* of a cube, and its quantity will be proportional to this surface, and so to r^2. But the total mass of matter inside the cube will be proportional to its volume, that is to r^3. Now as we imagine larger and larger cubes, the interaction between them will get less and less when considered in relation to the quantity of matter that they contain. That is to say, the larger they become, the more nearly will they approach isolation from the rest of the universe. In an infinite universe, we may consider indefinitely large cubes and so make them as isolated as we please. But since it is agreed that the entropy law would apply to each one of these isolated cubes taken separately, it must also apply to each one of an infinite number of them—that is, it applies to the whole universe.

[3] Readers of E. L. Mascall's *Christian Theology and Natural Science*, 1956, will have had a liberal dose of these doubts. Mascall can see no relation between the order found in energy (negative entropy or *negentropy*) and order of other kinds found in nature. (See later chapters of this book.) He seems unable to envisage the fact that negentropy is basic to the design of an ordered cosmos capable of supporting life. He would even cease to refer to *order* and *disorder* in connection with entropy, and replaces the words by "greater (or less) uniform" instead. But the alternative description is so meaningless to him that he can argue as follows: Energy and mass, he says, are conserved. So when they appear we say they are created. But entropy appears all the time. Does it need creating too? We expand a gas and new volume appears. Should we not say that volume requires a creator too? (p. 164). (The reader is led to wonder if entropy is an artefact.) Or again, since God is always active, His activity at the beginning of things "will not be essentially different from His activity at any other moment" (p. 148). (Astonishing temerity, this, to assert that God cannot,

Perhaps we may stress the point again—that the entropy law is a category of human thinking. Its truth is independent of whether, say, in a universe of such-and-such a kind, the particular mathematical expression used to calculate entropy increases as it should, or fails to do so. If mathematicians should ever prove that under certain unfamiliar conditions entropy decreases, most scientists will take this to mean, *not* that a one-way traffic in physical events is illusory (the equivalent of saying that events can occur backwards) but that disorder is not always adequately measured by the mathematical formula used to calculate entropy. And this would not be in the least surprising. We have noted how order may *appear* to be created, as in crystallisation. We have learned that this new order is balanced by loss of order in the energy of molecules. But in far away space, or cosmically "queer" conditions (e.g. in a pulsating universe during an epoch of contraction) an apparent rise in order might be balanced by other factors that mathematicians usually overlook. (Eg. The distribution of galaxies in space might become more random; electrical, magnetic or gravitational potentials might become more uniform; or it is conceivable that certain physical "constants" are not in reality constant for the whole of the universe but becomes more nearly so if the universe contracts or expands, etc.). There are, indeed, unlimited possibilities, normally excluded from discussion. A mathematical result which indicated a fall in entropy would be valueless unless *every* such possibility had been excluded. But all this is idle speculation. Taken as a whole, science gives the strongest imaginable support to the view that entropy *does* increase: in addition, if we do not assume this to be so, *all* science,[1] all rational thought even, becomes impossible—you cannot make science out of what you think you see in a nightmare, out of a disordered cosmos in which events future and past intertwine unpredictably.

[1] See R. E. D. Clark, *Jour. Trans. Victoria Instit.* 1943, **75**, 49; *Darwin: before and after,* 1958, Chap. 8.

at different times, be active in essentially different ways.) Mascall's conclusion follows, of course, from his premises—a meaningless gap in our knowledge concerning negentropy, he argues, in effect, cannot lead to a positive theological con-conclusion. So Aunt Sally is roundly defeated. The unfortunate "God of the gaps" —who never did exist anyway—is discreditied once more at the climax of a triumphal display of erudition.

CHANCE "WINDING" OF THE UNIVERSE

A second argument, inconsistent with the first, became popular after it was suggested by Professor J. B. S. Haldane many years ago. The entropy law turns out to be founded upon probability only. As we have seen, a very small number of objects may arrange themselves spontaneously in an ordered manner—three or four pebbles on the sand may lie in a straight line as a result of chance—but with larger numbers the probability that this kind of event will happen shrinks with great rapidity. Yet it is clear that the longer we wait, the greater will be the chance that such an arrangement will come into existence spontaneously. When we remember that a handful of matter contains not a few, but a million million million million molecules, it is obvious that we shall have to wait a very long time for these to fall into order of themselves. However, it may be supposed that occasionally, by a stupendous freak, a kettle will freeze when it is placed on the fire or cold water will start to boil without being heated. It is possible to calculate (though with no boast of great accuracy) how often events of this kind will take place and the chances of course prove to be very small indeed. They are so small that if the entire volume of the known universe were to be packed full of kettles, each kept under continuous observation by a guardian angel, it would still be most unlikely that even a single one of them would ever have been observed to behave in so freakish a manner since the day of creation. Indeed, the chances against one of them having done so, would still require many lines of noughts if it were to be written down on paper.

Nevertheless, we are cheerfully assured that given *infinite* time, such possibilities, however remote, must become certainties. Not only kettles, but even the entire universe must "wind itself up" occasionally. Nor should we hesitate to believe this theory on account of the enormous improbabilities which it presupposes, for unless we were living in an epoch just after the "self-winding" had taken place, we should not be here to tell the tale.

> There once was a brainy baboon,
> Who always blew down a bassoon.
>   For he said, "It appears
>   That in billions of years,
> I shall certainly hit on a tune."

Of course this argument is impossible to refute. With those who invoke the long arm of coincidence in a manner that is quite unrestrained, argument is impossible—for they remain unimpressed by every proof that the arm is inordinately long!

However, before jumping to the conclusion that this is a point in favour of this argument, it is important to realize what is involved.

First of all, with regard to evolution. If it is very improbable that one kettle full of water will start to boil by chance, it is more improbable still that two of them will do so. Since the universe is "running down" it follows that the further we go back in time, the more improbable is the state of affairs that we encounter. The freak of the "self-winding" of the universe becomes a greater and greater freak, the greater the degree to which we imagine the process of "re-winding" to have been carried. It is incalculably more probable that the universe "wound" itself up by chance to produce the state of affairs that we find today, than that it should have "wound" itself up to produce the state of affairs which we reckon to have existed say a million or a hundred million years ago. If, then, we are prepared to take the "self-winding" suggestion seriously, there is no need whatever to believe the story that scientists tell us about the past history of our planet. The odds are quite overwhelmingly in favour of the view that, if the universe wound itself up at all, it did so quite a short time ago, perhaps last night, perhaps yesterday. Our memories of the apparent past might very well be explained as freaks, as may also the books and buildings which we generally associate with former generations. Fossils, of course, present even fewer difficulties. There seems no reason why they should not have been produced by the freakish coming together of atoms and molecules in the rocks as was, indeed, once thought to have been the case. Likewise, the arguments for evolution on our planet go by the board—the chances that no such evolution took place being enormously greater than the chances that it did.

As Eddington pointed out,[1] the chance theory of the universe undermines the ground of science itself. If it is true that natural events, as we know them, represent only what happens during an exceedingly short instant relative to infinite time, and at an instant of a *highly exceptional* nature, then we may as well shut up shop as far as science is concerned. For it is hard to see why we should have any confidence in our measurements and observations if they

[1] A. S. Eddington, *New Pathways in Science*, 1935, p. 64.

relate only to what is happening during an excessively rare statistical fluctuation. Surely, one might as well seek to gain an idea of how the cogs of a car function by observing their behaviour within a fraction of a second after the car had been hit by a bomb. Science depends for its existence upon the assumption that nature offers us a fair sample of herself to study and the idea that we are living at a moment during infinite time when a chance fluctuation has set the normal course of events into topsy-turvydom, under-mines scientific law and order at its foundations.

Eddington also pointed out, again very aptly, that if ever water were observed to boil of its own accord, no reasonable person would think of invoking chance as the explanation, but would be far more likely to invoke a supernatural agency! It seems unfair, therefore, to use an argument about the universe which one would not think of using about a kettle![1]

A cogent answer to the theory that the universe arose by chance has also been given by Bridgman, who points out that mathematics can give us no warrant whatever for assuming either that water will freeze or boil by chance or that the universe will ever wind itself up—even in infinite time.

Bridgman argues in the following way. Calculation shows that, if we throw a coin about 1,400 times, there is an even chance that we shall obtain a run of ten consecutive heads. But we may obtain a series of ten heads long before we have completed a thousand throws. Can we attribute this result to chance? Or may it have been caused by unfair throwing or by a bias in the coin? Our only way to find out is to throw the coin a large number of times so as to confirm that, in the long run, the heads and tails are about equal in number. But how many throws will be necessary? The answer comes out to be around a thousand or so. Drawing the conclusion from this, we may quote Bridgman's words, "In order to establish with sufficient probability that the actual physical system has those properties which are assumed in estimating the frequency of rare occurrences, it is necessary to make a number of observations so great that the proba-bility is good that the rare occurrence has already been observed. In other words purely logical statistical considerations never can justify us in predicting events so rare that they have never yet been observed.

[1] The late Mr. Harry Price, an authority on everything extraordinary, maintained that a saucepan in a house in Leamington in 1929, which contained water and peeled potatoes, boiled over in the middle of the night for no apparent reason. So Eddington's hypothetical possibility may not be so hypothetical after all! (*Polter-geist Over England*, 1945, p. 335).

A pail of water has never yet been observed to freeze on the fire; statistical considerations give us no warrant whatever for expecting that it ever will."[1]

These considerations would seem to be of so serious a nature that it is surprising that anyone can take the chance theory seriously. Yet some rationalist writers not only argue in its favour, but also argue that only obscurantists deny the theory of evolution. They seem blissfully unaware that they themselves have undermined the only argument upon which the theory of evolution can rest.

EXPANDING UNIVERSE

We have summarized most of the one-time fashionable arguments relating to entropy. Something must now be said about a new one. It runs like this.

If the universe is infinite but is expanding into space, both its energy and its material are becoming increasingly scattered. Disorder is, then, increasing. There *might,* however, be a compensating process—a local, perhaps even cosmic, piling up of energy which compensates for the increasing dispersion into space. There would, of course, be no contravention of physical law if the entropy of the universe as a whole, instead of increasing, stayed constant.

If the universe is finite and expanding, it means that the galaxies are slowing down as their kinetic energy turns into potential energy. This process cannot go on for ever—in time the process will reverse—the universe will contract to its former state. After that it will explode once more. In fact, the universe will become cyclical—exploding and contracting eternally.[2] The Greek view in modern guise!

We are on dangerous ground here, speculating far beyond the confines of knowledge. But it is fair to argue that such speculations

[1] P. W. Bridgman, *Science*, 1932, **75**, 419. The inconsistency involved in the arguments of many agnostic apologists will be at once apparent. As a rule they (1) object to the application of the entropy law to the entire universe on the ground that it is illogical to make far-flung extrapolations; yet (2) they are often quite prepared to extrapolate from our very limited experience of statistical fluctuations in order to deduce that the universe is the result of such a fluctuation! It is refreshing to note that the communist writer A. I. Oparin (*The Origin of Life on the Earth*, 1957, pp. 95 ff.) argues strongly that since the chance argument (applied to the origin of life) undermines science it cannot be maintained. But he has nothing concrete to offer in its place. See later, p. 140.

[2] As suggested, for example, by E. J. Opik, *British Jour. Philos. Sci.* 1954, **5**, 203.

are based upon precisely nothing—not even irresponsible extrapolation. If an increase in order in one place is exactly compensated for by an increase in disorder in another, some specialized mechanism is called for. The process must be one which thermodynamicians call *reversible*. No hint of the existence of such a mechanism has been discovered in space or on earth. And if it existed, it seems even doubtful if the entropy law would have been discovered.

It seems evident that a cyclic universe would not last for ever—explosions and contractions would fizzle out in time and all would be tranquil. Creation might have happened earlier than we had supposed—that is all!

CONTINUOUS CREATION

According to a widely popularized theory of the universe (Hoyle, Bondi,[1] etc.), matter is in a state of continuous creation. It is supposed that either neutrons or hydrogen atoms are being introduced from nowhere throughout the whole volume of space, and that they are subsequently attracted towards galaxies and stars, thus providing them with a continuous supply of energy. The rate at which new atoms appear is, admittedly, much too small for observation ever to confirm or refute the theory—but then it is pointed out that *every* theory of the universe involves the unobservable—in particular no one can observe an original creation. To some extent it is a question of where and when we suppose that unobservable events take place.

Much ingenious speculation and mathematical work has been developed in connexion with this hypothesis. It is generally felt, however, that it suffers from too many difficulties to win general acceptance. Present observational evidence on radio-stars seems to indicate that the universe has *not* settled down to a steady state. At great distances we "see" (by the radio waves emitted) stars at past epochs in time—owing to the enormous periods taken for their messages to reach us. If the universe is "exploding", then at earlier epochs the stars must have been more closely clustered than now. On the other hand, if the universe has reached a steady state, and especially if it is eternal, the density of stars will not vary with

[1] F. Hoyle, *Frontiers of Astronomy*, 1955; *The Nature of the Universe*, 1960. H. Bondi, *Cosmology*, 1952. Etc. It is my understanding that Hoyle later abandoned the theory, although it is still uncertain whether he has done so.

time. At the moment of writing observational evidence favours the former view (Ryle, 1961), quite strongly so. Moreover, the original reason for the development of the continuous creation theory has now disappeared—the supposed fact that the earth is older than the universe as calculated from the speed of recession of the nebulae. In earlier estimates the distance of the nebulae was underestimated but the discrepancy no longer exists.

But science is full of surprises. So let us suppose the position reversed—let us suppose that the doctrine of continuous creation were proved. What then?

Continuous creation, of course, cheats entropy. But then it cheats all round. Mass and energy together are no longer constant—even new rotation and acceleration might occur without observable cause. Continuous creation does not avoid creation—it merely spreads it liberally over the whole of time and space. And if, in our universe, we find anything that seems purposeful and designed, the purpose will not evaporate if provided in small doses rather than in one large creative act.

It may be added, however, that the two conceptions are not necessarily contradictory. As developed by Hoyle and Bondi, there was no sudden creation at the beginning, and the universe is infinite. But the theory could, almost certainly, have equally well been developed by supposing that there had been an original creation and that this was followed by "continuous creation" which has persisted ever since..

BEFORE CREATION

Something may now be said about attempts to think behind the creation epoch. Such attempts are, of course, in no way new to our day. Even in Newton's time, the idea was current that the universe once consisted of a diffuse gas and it was suggested that the newly discovered gravitational attraction would cause this gas to condense into stars. Herbert Spencer developed the same theme in the nineteenth century.

In the past it has never been possible to explain in this way the two most obvious features of the visible universe. First of all there is the co-existence of high and low temperatures and, secondly, the fact of rotation. Today, it would, perhaps, be possible to understand how high temperatures might be produced, for atomic chain reactions generating heat would probably start when sufficiently large quantities of matter had collected together. No way of evading the second difficulty has, however, been suggested. Herbert Spencer was even led to deny the truth of one of the best established physical laws (the law of the conservation of angular momentum[1]) as a result of his enthusiasm to represent the universe as the product of blind chance.

A satisfactory theory of the origin of the universe must account not only for the two points mentioned but also for a number of other facts, such as the expansion of the universe (now generally accepted as a fact) and its chemical composition.

Now we might reasonably suppose that a primitive gas in space would contain atoms of all the ninety-two elements. But if so, there would seem to be no obvious reason why the amounts of these elements should be connected with one another. Actually it is found that, as the weights of the atoms increase, their amount falls

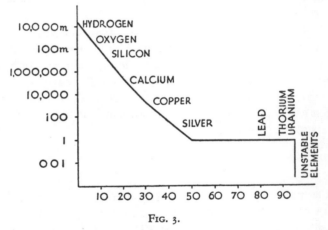

FIG. 3.

Diagram showing how the relative abundance of the elements varies with the weight of their atoms. (The logarithm of the abundance is plotted against the atomic number). Most elements fall approximately on the curve shown but there is a marked tendency for even and odd elements to fall somewhat above and below the line alternately, elements with even atomic numbers being commoner than those with odd. (*m* is used as an abbreviation for *million*.)

[1] This, like other laws of mechanics, is a particular case of the (generalised) entropy law or law of morpholysis (see p. 23). We may always think of a rotating body as being at rest, relatively, to itself. If, then, it spontaneously alters its rotation (gains rotation relative to its former state), its parts acquire a new co-ordinated motion—i.e. order is gained spontaneously, which is contrary to the entropy law.

steadily (in a series of "ups" and "downs"—each "odd" element being rarer than the "even" elements on either side of it) until we reach a position (near that of silver) about half-way up the scale. After that there is, if anything, a slight rise in the abundance of the elements—though the quantities of the heavier elements do not vary very greatly from one another.

The amounts of the simpler elements suggest strongly that they were once in equilibrium. Possibly they have all been built up from hydrogen and although it appears fairly certain that this cannot happen in an ordinary star, such as the sun, it is possible that this equilibrium is in process of being established in certain very hot stars or, perhaps, only in *novae*.

The origin of the heavy elements, lead, gold, the radioactive elements and so on, appears to present much greater difficulties. Perhaps the universe was once the nucleus of a single gigantic atom —an atom which was composed of neutrons only. This "atom" need only have been about six million miles in diameter and, in one stupendous expansion, which is still continuing to this day, it may have shattered into fragments (the present atoms) and given rise to the whole visible universe. According to another view heavy elements are born as a result of the huge transitory temperatures and pressures that occur inside exploding *super-novae*.[1]

Obviously the whole subject is in the melting pot and there it is likely to stay for a long time. But to take stock of the situation, modern research has made it abundantly clear that however the universe started—whether as a diffuse or a highly compressed gas —it did not start in a disordered but in an exceedingly highly ordered state. Pushing difficulties back to a pre-creation epoch can do nothing to avoid the creation of the universe. Sir Isaac Newton pointed this out in his own day when he argued that, supposing the current theory of an original diffuse gas to be correct, the state of that gas must have been either stable or unstable. If it was stable, it would have needed a miracle to turn it into the universe. On the other hand, if it was unstable, we must postulate a miracle of another kind that prevented the matter from congregating to form stars at an earlier epoch. This logic would appear to be unassailable.

---

[1] For these speculations the *Astrophysical Journal* and *Monthly Notices of the Royal Astronomical Society* for recent years may be consulted. For the exploding "atom" theory see G. Gamow, *The Creation of the Universe*, N.Y., 1952.

DATE OF CREATION

Ignoring, for the moment, the theory of continuous creation, we reach the conclusion that at some point or epoch in past time events took place which differed completely from those that are happening in our day.   Practically all of the laws of science with which we are familiar are more or less disguised forms of the statement that disorder increases spontaneously. Yet the reverse of this process must somehow have taken place—unless, indeed, all matter in a highly organized state was suddenly created from nothing by a fiat of Divine will.

Even if we accept continuous creation, our conclusion is hardly altered. For continuous creation only means that now, *as also in past time,* hidden events take place, or took place, which again differ radically in kind from those which we can observe and which form the basis of our science.

Evidence for the conclusion that the universe was "created" in time—a conclusion which now seems to be highly probable—has also come in other ways so that today the evidence for a creation no longer rests upon entropy alone but also upon a number of other less important lines of argument. The existence of radioactive materials which cannot have been decomposing for ever, the dynamics of the star clusters, double stars and planets which have not yet had time to come into equilibrium since they first came into being: the fact that spiral nebulae seem only to have had time to rotate two and a half times since they were formed: considerations based upon the light given out by stars and their present fuel (hydrogen) supply: the expansion of the universe: estimates of the age of the oldest rocks—all these methods seem to date the "creation" at between one and ten thousand million years ago—with a most probable figure about eight thousand million.

By making suitable assumptions the figure can, of course, be raised. Thus Lemaître supposed that a primeval atom exploded 20 to 60 thousand million years ago but that our present galaxies did not begin to form and expand until about nine thousand million years ago. The basic idea of an original creation is, of course, unchanged.

IMPORTANCE OF CREATION

Today, perhaps, this conclusion is so familiar that it has long since ceased to surprise us. We find it difficult to think ourselves back into ancient and medieval times when reason seemed to indicate that nature involved an eternal cycle of events. However this may be, the direction which scientific research has taken throughout the past century is so interesting that it is worth a passing comment.

In the old days, the universe seemed to offer little mystery and it appeared quite possible that man would soon be enabled to comprehend it. The same was true, even in the nineteenth century, when a primitive fire mist was supposed to account adequately for the existence of the universe. Since then the mystery has steadily deepened until, today, we can only say that the epoch of creation makes a mock of all our ideas of cause and effect and of physical law. Intellectually it appears to lead us only to an impasse.

Finally, let us take stock of the situation. Science teaches us two things. It teaches us that all ordinary events in nature—all the law and uniformity with which we are familiar—are connected with and, indeed, generally occasioned by, the disordering of atoms or of energy. But it teaches us no less emphatically that there was once a time when not a single law with which we are familiar could have operated at all. At this period or moment of creation, the events which took place must have been of a kind precisely opposite to anything we should have predicted—every one of the generalizations in which we place our confidence must not only have failed completely but must have been outrageously "disobeyed". We are apt to think of creation as an exception and, anyway, since it happened so long ago, it may seem of little practical importance to us.[1] These are points to which we shall have reason to refer again. But meanwhile we may observe that since every one of our present laws of science only describes the undoing of what happened at the

---

[1] To ignore creation, because of the remoteness of the creation epoch, would be the height of unreason. Evolutionary humanists, such as Sir Julian Huxley and Père Teilhard de Chardin (*The Phenomenon of Man,* 1959), who virtually deify the evolutionary principle, do not seem in the least put out by the hundreds of millions of years involved. If we are the products of evolution, they argue, then evolution is important and the time scale is irrelevant. But by parity of reasoning, creation is much more important.

creation, it is hardly sensible to regard the latter as in any way unimportant. Were we to live in a house that was constantly falling into disrepair, we might succeed in formulating rules which would enable us to predict, with fair success, when slates would fall from the roof, doors come off their hinges or plaster fall from the ceilings. Or, if our ability to predict were more limited, we might at least be able to say that the annual cost of repairs for a few years ahead was likely to be so and so. In this way we should be able to build up a rudimentary "science" of disrepair, but our newly invented "science" would hardly lead us to regard the original building of the house as an "exceptional" and therefore unimportant affair, nor should we be any more inclined to argue in this way if the house was very old. The analogy is apt: it is clear that creation cannot fairly be dismissed from our philosophy. It was a happening so important that there is scarcely an event in the physical world of today which does not consist of an undoing of what happened then. Nor does it make a whit of difference, if continuous creation occurs now—for every atom we encounter must still have had its creation epoch, even if different atoms were created at different times.

It is reasonable, then, to allow the idea of creation to dominate our thinking. Creation—which we may accept at this stage simply as the reverse of all scientific laws (leaving discussion of its purposive aspects till later)—is by far the most important fact of which we have cognizance. Other facts, theories and hypotheses—the constancy of the laws of nature, the theory of evolution, the importance of scientific method, and so on—are of trite importance by comparison. Nor can any one of them become central to our thinking. But for creation there would be *no* scientific laws, *no* theory of evolution, *no* science, indeed *no* men to think!

What, then, can we learn by recognizing creation as a fact? Before we attempt to answer this question we shall look first to see whether other branches of science can help us in our quest.

CHAPTER III

WORLDS WITHOUT END

THE last two chapters have served to introduce the subject of astronomy. We have seen that astronomy, like physics, points strongly to a "creation" at the beginning of time. But astronomy has also been concerned, from time immemorial, with another aspect of philosophy. Is this world of ours the only world of its kind? Are there reasons to think that it occupies a place of special importance in the scheme of things? Was the earth so fashioned as to make life possible upon its surface, or is it but one of an immense number of worlds formed as a result of time and chance?

As we turn to consider these questions we must not expect the science of any one age to provide us with final answers. There are, no doubt, imaginative enthusiasts who suppose that inter-planetary travel by rocket propulsion will one day enable the universe to be adequately explored, but that at all events cannot be in our day! Nevertheless, the subject is one of such absorbing interest that we shall assuredly find ourselves amply repaid if we linger a while to consider some of the views that have been held upon this subject both in the past and at the present time.

IMAGINATIVE GREEKS

In one form or another, the pleasant fancy that there are thousands upon thousands of other worlds like ours, has engaged the minds of men for millenniums.

We meet the conjecture first among the Greeks, where it had a long history and flowered, at various times, in a great diversity of forms. According to the view most widely held, each world had its own sun, moon and stars, each of these systems being enclosed, as it were, in a kind of celestial package.

Many of the Greeks believed that these world-systems were almost infinite in number and that each one precisely resembled our own. There were others, however, who denied this identity

and claimed that all kinds of variations were to be found—some of
the world-systems had no moon, others had two suns and so on.
Democritus, for instance, claimed that some of the worlds were
smaller and some larger than the earth, while at any given time
some were thriving and some decaying. Not all of them had
inhabitants—some were devoid of animals, plants and even
water.[1] He believed too that with the passing of the aeons many
of them would be destroyed by colliding with one another.

In addition to these speculations, many of the Greeks suggested
that our own moon was inhabited. It is said that the Pythagorians,
for instance, believed that "the moon is terraneous, is inhabited as
our world is, and contains animals of a larger size and plants of a
rarer beauty than our globe affords. The animals in their virtue
and energy are fifteen degrees superior to ours, emit nothing excre-
mentitious, and the days are fifteen times longer."

To us these views appear only in the guise of unbridled speculations. Not so to the ancients. In those days the entire universe was
supposed to be constructed according to a single plan which
enabled truth about one part of it to be discovered by arguments
based on analogies with another part. In a different form the same
presupposition still largely underlies science. Whereas Metrodorus
wrote: "It seems absurd that in a large field only one stalk should
grow, and in an infinite space only one world exist," the modern
physicist would apply much the same reasoning, not indeed to
plants and worlds, but to the laws of science which he has proved
to possess validity on earth.

The doctrine of the plurality of worlds suffered a serious setback
at the hands of Plato who maintained that it could only be accepted
by people with crassly ignorant and sadly inventive minds. In later
years the criticisms of Aristotle were no less severe—indeed,
Aristotle claimed to have disproved the doctrine once and for all.
His proof, which is of some interest, proceeded as follows:

The stars and with them the whole of space, the entire universe in
fact, revolve round the earth. It follows that the universe cannot be

[1] In an interesting paper (*The Scientist's Playground*, Proc. Royal Society of
Medicine, February 1937), W. H. S. Jones has suggested that the wilder guesses
of the Greeks were akin to our games of chess, our delight in fiction, our visits to
the cinema and our crossword puzzles. In speculating on matters which could not
at that time be related to hard fact the Greeks found a release, though often perhaps
almost unconsciously, from the world of reality.

infinite, for infinite things cannot move and so cannot revolve. Therefore, there cannot be an infinite number of worlds. But suppose there
is even one other world such as ours. It, too, must necessarily possess
a complement of stars revolving round it. Therefore, between that
world-system and ours there must be empty space for, if this were
not so, the second world-system would form part of our own world-
system since it would be revolving round us like one of the stars. But
nature abhors a vacuum so that empty space of this kind is impossible.
It follows, therefore, that there can only be one world.

This curious argument—an argument which is no longer
plausible today—was considered final by Aristotle and his contemporaries and was appealed to again and again, during the course of
subsequent ages.

THE CHURCH AND THE PLURALITY OF WORLDS

For a long time Aristotle's views were adopted both by pagans
and Christians. The early and later Fathers inveighed against the
doctrine of the plurality of worlds: it is related that in the eighth
century a learned bishop was deprived of his see and suffered the
dire penalty of excommunication for maintaining that there was
just one other world besides our own. It is hard, looking back, to
understand why anyone should have wished to become a martyr for
such a cause!

With the passing of the years ecclesiastical opposition to the
plurality of worlds grew in intensity. St. Thomas Aquinas, who
revived the science of Aristotle, added yet a further proof that
other worlds did not exist, to the proof that Aristotle had already
furnished. His proof, which runs as follows, is typical of his way
of reasoning.

If God had made any other worlds, they must either be similar or
dissimilar to this one. If they are similar, God can have had no
object in making them and it is inconceivable that God would have
done anything in vain. But if they are dissimilar, no one of them
can contain all things and, therefore, no one of them can be perfect.
So, the perfect Creator must have made worlds which are imperfect
and this is contrary to sound reason. Therefore, if God has made any
other worlds, they are neither similar nor dissimilar to our world,
which is, of course, impossible. It follows, therefore, that our own

world is the only one He has created. Indeed, said St. Thomas, anyone who maintains the contrary opinion is self-confessedly a
materialist who does not believe that God has made the world at all.

By and by the theologians undermined their own opinions as a
result of their very ardour to defend them. They were gradually
driven to the conclusion that God could not have made any other
worlds even if He had wished to do so!

In time this inevitably produced a strong reaction. In 1277 the
Church condemned the doctrine that God could not have made as
many worlds as He pleased. So once again men were free to toy
with the idea that there might be other worlds like ours scattered
throughout the universe. By 1400 opposition to such speculations
had died down almost completely and did not revive for a century
and a half.

THE CHURCH AND ASTRONOMY

Much has been written on the subject of astronomy and the
Christian faith. Rationalist propagandists have long been in the
habit of representing the Church as engaged in a continual warfare
with science and as being opposed to the work of the pioneers in
astronomical science—Bruno, Copernicus and Galileo.

It is true that Bruno was burned at the stake and that one of the
charges against him was that he held unorthodox views on
astronomy. But there were other much more serious indictments
too. He was accused of being a runaway monk and of denying the
doctrines of transubstantiation and of the Virgin Birth. He had
written a book called *On the Triumph of the Beast* and had made
it quite clear that the Beast in question was the Pope. He was
accused, too, of having spoken in high praise of Luther, of having
written in praise of Elizabeth of England and other heretical rulers
and of being a leader among heretics.[1] Besides such charges we
may be quite certain that that relating to astronomy did not loom
very large. Nor is it clear that the issue of the movement of the
earth round the sun was specifically raised—for Bruno held that
the universe was infinite and could not therefore, so he claimed,
have been created by God. His doctrine, in fact, was essentially
pantheistic and his belief in the plurality of worlds was quite a

[1] See for example, H. Keston, *Copernicus and his World*, 1946, p. 328.

side-line. He did not suffer for making astronomical discoveries but for holding opinions which were quite unrelated to ascertained fact. Nevertheless, since Bruno had been so insistent upon his belief in the plurality of worlds, it was natural that the Church began once more to question its orthodoxy!

This became one of the chief issues in the days of Galileo. For the discovery of Jupiter and its moons seemed to Galileo's contemporaries like the discovery of a new solar system and, naturally enough, they found it hard to believe that the moons were not inhabited. Astronomy, therefore, became dangerous and it must have seemed doubly so when, later on, Galileo broke his promise and published his famous *Two Dialogues* in which he deliberately put the words of the Pope into the mouth of a simple fool—Simplicius! Nevertheless, Galileo was treated with great consideration and it appears that the threat of torture was finally made only in a formal manner and was not understood by him to have been intended seriously.

In the entire controversy the real issues at stake were obviously of much greater importance than the question of the movement of the earth around the sun. Christians in the Middle Ages had found no difficulty in reconciling themselves to the view that the earth was round—its roundness had long been taught in the medieval schools. The discovery that it moved round the sun would not, of itself, have created any additional difficulty. But the ideas that the universe was *infinite* and that every star in the sky was inhabited were much more serious. The first seemed to cut at the root of the belief that the universe had been created while the second made it more difficult to believe that God cared to any great extent about the inhabitants of the earth.

IRRESPONSIBLE SPECULATION

The fears of the Papacy were not unfounded. No sooner had Galileo spread his views in popular books than speculation about the inhabitants of other parts of the universe began in earnest. Irresponsible and imaginative space fiction poured from the printing presses of Europe and the wildest fancies were indulged. Strange and mythical creatures were freely invented with bodies that enabled them to live in every imaginable physical environment. Before long there was almost general agreement that the moon was inhabited as were also all the planets and even the sun itself. Every star in the sky was supposed to possess its bevy of planets, all of them inhabited. And such views came to be held, not only by the populace at large but by eminent astronomers who, at that time, were well disposed towards all views that were calculated to create wonder and excitement among ordinary people.

Among the well-known men of the day, Kepler at first rejected these ideas but later changed his mind and became reasonably sure that the moon, Jupiter and even the sun, were populated.

John Wilkins decided that all the planets were inhabited. Huygens, too, said they were "Stock'd with Plants and Animals," and declared that on every one of them there were civilized beings. In like manner the pious John Ray, in his *Wisdom of God* (1709) argued that "there are infinite other Creatures without this earth, which no considerate Man can think were made only for man : and have no other use. . . . For it seems to me highly absurd and un- reasonable, to think that Bodies of such vast magnitude as the fix'd Stars, were only made to twinkle to us; nay, a multitude of them there are that do not so much as twinkle."[1]

Often, of course, the contrary opinion was also expressed. Indeed, it was urged that the plurality of worlds was a view so ridiculous—a "prodigious paradox" as Robert Burton was pleased to call it—that the mere fact that Copernican astronomy lent colour to it was enough to discredit the Copernican theory in the eyes of every right-minded person!

CHRISTIAN VIEWS CONFIRMED

In time, of course, the Copernican view came to be generally accepted. Nor was it felt to be contrary to Christian thought. The Bible often strains language to the utmost in its attempts to show how small a place the earth really is. The entire world is like a footstool to the Most High (Isaiah 66: 1; Acts 7: 49); God dwells on high and has to humble Himself even to look at earthly things (Psalm 113: 6); "Behold, the nations are as a drop of a bucket, and are counted as the small dust of the balance. . . . All the nations are as nothing before Him; they are counted to Him less

---

[1] Further information on the early history of the doctrine of the plurality of worlds will be found in G. McColley's valuable monograph (*Annals of Science*, 1936, Vol. I, 385), on which the above account is based.

than nothing and vanity"—the inhabitants of the earth are mere grasshoppers in His sight (Isaiah 40: 15–22). Such truths found factual confirmation in the new views that were being propounded about the universe. And when astronomers found that eclipses and comets were subject to the ordinary laws of nature, instead of being harbingers of wrath, Christians had even less to fear. Astronomy was now confirming the words of the prophet: "Be not dismayed at the signs of heaven; for the heathen are dismayed at them" (Jeremiah 10: 2).

It soon became clear that, although the new discoveries of astronomy were doing much to undermine the authority of Aristotle, they were tending to confirm Christian views rather than the reverse. And thinking men came to realize that, as telescopes revealed more and more of the heavenly realms to the eyes of man, so there were greater reasons than ever for worshipping the Creator who had made all these marvels.

SENSATIONS OF LATER DAYS

In the eighteenth century the excitement occasioned by the doctrine of the plurality of worlds died down: the novelty of the subject had worn thin. Yet, from that time onwards, sensations have not been altogether lacking. A new turn to the discussion was given by Immanuel Swedenborg, who solemnly asserted that he had frequently conversed with the lunar and planetary inhabitants! Since his day spiritualists and others have frequently made similar claims, the famous nineteenth-century girl, Hélène Smith, being able to talk fluently in Martian! In 1835 the *New York Sun* published a series of articles, which purported to be an account of the astronomical investigations of Sir John Herschel who was then at the Cape of Good Hope. It was said that the article was reprinted from a supplement to the *Edinburgh Journal of Science*— a supplement, the existence of which was, of course, purely mythical. A circumstantial account was given of how a new telescope with a 24-foot object glass had been constructed, which weighed seven tons after polishing. With this new instrument and a wonderful system of "hydro-oxygen reflectors" (!) Sir John had left for the Cape. Since then no more had been heard of him until a letter reached Vienna to say;

that the portentous comet predicted for the year 1835, which was to approach so near the trembling globe that we might hear the roaring of its fires, had turned upon another scent, and would not even shake a hair of its tail upon our hunting-grounds.

There followed a long and marvellous description of objects seen on the moon, among which "men" could be clearly delineated:

> They averaged four feet in height, were covered, except on the face, with short and glossy copper-coloured hair, and had wings composed of a thin membrane, without hair, lying snugly upon their backs, from the top of the shoulders to the calves of the legs." The creatures could be seen, at times, to talk and their faces were "open and intelligent in expression". They had built a beautiful temple out of polished sapphire. "They were never observed in the act of working; instead they spent their happy hours collecting various fruits in the woods, in eating, flying, bathing and loitering about upon the summits of precipices." After improvements in the apparatus had been carried out it was hoped to investigate the lunar insects and other lowly forms of life.

As a result of these "revelations" the circulation of the *New York Sun* rose five-fold and, for the first time, the journal gained a permanent footing as a daily newspaper.

Despite these and other puerilities, the doctrine of the plurality of worlds once again found a place in orthodox science. It was accepted by most of the popularizers of science in the nineteenth century, including Ray Lankester, Herbert Spencer, Proctor, Flammarion and Arrhenius. In his book, *Star Land,* Sir Robert Ball summarized what most of his own generation of astronomers thought about the matter.

> I do not think that any reasonable person will doubt that there must be inhabitants elsewhere. There are millions of globes, many of them more splendid than ours. Surely it would be presumptuous to say that this is the only one of all the bodies in the universe on the surface of which life, with all that life involves, is manifested?

IS MAN ALONE?

Not until 1853 did the discussion begin to be seriously debated on the basis of ascertained fact. In that year Dr. William Whewell wrote an anonymous but important book in which he pointed out that the earth's orbit is situated in the "temperate zone" of the solar system—the only part in which life, as we know it, is capable of existence. But Whewell was greatly concerned lest his novel idea should offend his readers who might well fear that the "field of God's greatness, benevolence and government, had been narrowed and impoverished, to an extent painful and shocking by such views." It was for this reason that he did not at first reveal his authorship.

Towards the end of his book Whewell discussed the physical conditions pertaining on the various planets and argued, for instance, that if any creatures existed on Saturn, they were at the best "aqueous, gelatinous creatures; too sluggish almost to be deemed alive, floating in their ice-cold waters, shrouded for ever by their humid skies". On Mars alone did he consider that there was a possibility of life more highly developed than that of jelly-fish.

Whewell's warning voice was little heeded by his contemporaries. In the following year the pious Sir David Brewster replied with the traditional arguments to the effect that life might well adapt itself to conditions unfamiliar to us. Why should we limit life by our own limited experience? he asked. There were no sound reasons, he said, for supposing that life could not adapt itself to an icy-cold or even a red-hot environment. Nor need we imagine that it is in any way limited by the presence of an atmosphere.

There the matter largely rested until, in 1903, Alfred Russel Wallace published his remarkable book *Man's Place in the Universe*. In this book the arguments of Whewell were again brought forward and it was pointed out that they were strongly supported by the discoveries in astronomy that had been made since Whewell's day. Wallace laid the foundations of modern thinking on the subject, to which we shall now turn.

CHAPTER IV

"VARIETIES OF CREATURES . . ."

AS we have already had occasion to note, discussions on the possibility of life in other parts of the universe have largely centred round the question of how far life can adapt itself to conditions wholly different from those with which we are familiar on earth.

Life on earth shows an amazing variety. We find it on mountains, in valleys, on plains and in both salt and fresh water. Most living organisms flourish in air but there are others such as yeast cells and many bacteria, which can perform their functions in absence of oxygen while, among the autotrophic bacteria, we find organisms that can obtain their energy from a great variety of chemical reactions.

Again, we see evidences of the same astonishing adaptability within the organs of a single animal. The material out of which the intestine is made can live indefinitely in contact with gastric juices which will disintegrate practically all other forms of living matter: the blood can immunize itself so as to be capable of resisting the influence of foreign infections and so on. In short, life possesses a quite astonishing power of adapting itself to strange and unusual conditions. But how far can such adaptation proceed?

In the early days it was easy and natural to extrapolate. It must once have seemed that the earth contained all extremes of heat and cold, of pressure and of chemical environment. Scholars were unaware of the fact that nature knew of cold far more intense than anything to be experienced in Russia or Antarctica and of heat far hotter than flame. Adaptations of life to different conditions on earth were so striking that it may well have seemed reasonable to suppose that such adaptations would have to go but a *little* further to cover all conditions that were likely to be encountered in the entire universe.

Perhaps it is along some such lines as these that we may seek to defend the ideas of the older scientists and scholars that sound so strange today. For the ancients seem to have been convinced that there was one animal at least—the salamander—which was capable of living happily in the midst of the hottest fire. In support of this view they urged that it was a matter of experience that fire does not destroy all things—gold and ashes, for instance—and therefore there was no clear reason why it should destroy all forms of life.

At one time, too, it was commonly supposed that fire-flies were not only unharmed by fire, but were actually generated in the flame —the entire world's supply of them coming from the brass furnaces in the Isle of Cyprus. Even in the seventeenth century we find the learned Moffett still maintaining this view in his portly *History of Four-footed Beasts and Serpents* (1658):

> When Agricola affirmeth that the fire-fly is generated in this fire of ours, I see no reason why any should doubt of it: yet there are some very learned men and eminent writers of our time . . . who condemn and reject not only the generation of these little creatures in the fire, but this whole history as frivolous, false, and unworthy of a philosopher.

At the time when the beginnings of modern astronomy once again occasioned unbridled speculations concerning the plurality of worlds, it was natural that the old views concerning salamanders and fire-flies should have taken on a new interest. If creatures on earth could live and breed in fire, it was only natural to suppose that innumerable forms of life might dwell in stars and planets. Saturn, said William Molyneux (1693) was very cold and Mercury scorched with heat but that mattered little for there were doubtless "varieties of creatures . . . some adapted to one Planet, others to others."

CELESTIAL MATTER

There was another way, too, in which the views held by the ancients helped to foster these wild speculations. It had always been imagined that the matter out of which the sun and stars were composed was of a totally different kind from that with which we on earth are familiar. Celestial matter was *pure*[1]: terrestrial matter

[1] This view was not held by the ancient Hebrews. "The stars are not pure in his sight" (Job. 25: 5).

was *impure*. It was this notion that Galileo did so much to refute when he discovered spots on the sun—for it did not at all tally with the Aristotelian view of things that a pure body should be defiled by spots.

Nevertheless, despite the views of the early astronomers, the old way of thinking was deeply ingrained—nor has it been entirely eradicated, even to this day. For centuries the argument continued to be used that, for all we know, matter in other parts of the universe is of a kind totally different from the matter with which we are familiar. While, therefore, it was easy enough to agree that animals made out of our matter might have a poor expectation of life if they were deported to the sun, yet solar animals, made out of genuine solar matter, might be supremely contented in their fiery surroundings.

CHEMISTRY IS UNIVERSAL

Developments in science over the past century or so have, however, removed any plausibility that such speculations may once have had. Long ago, when the spectroscope was applied to astronomical research, it was at once found that the elements with which we are familiar on earth exist also in the stars and, indeed, in the farthest nebulae. One by one the spectral lines have been identified until, today, the presence of two-thirds of the elements has been definitely established in the sun including many, such as gold, that are of great rarity. Of the remaining a few cannot be detected only on account of the fact that they give no spectrum in the visible range. Much progress has also been achieved towards identifying curious spectral lines which for long defied analysis—particularly those found in the light of the sun's *corona* (due to common elements, such as calcium, iron and nickel) and in the *novae* and *super-novae*. Many of these lines can be seen in the explosions of nuclear devices and their unusual character is the result of the enormous temperatures involved.

In addition to the light which comes to us from beyond the solar system, meteorites, too, often bring their message. These also confirm our belief that the matter of the universe is of one kind only, for they turn out to be composed of familiar elements.

There has, of late, been some discussion concerning *anti-matter* —matter with its electric charges reversed. It is suggested that, at the creation epoch, matter and anti-matter might have been formed in equal amounts so that pockets of anti-matter may be present still. Matter and anti-matter explode when they come into contact —one suggestion is that meteorites of anti-matter have been responsible for those which have caused unusually violent explosions. All this is pure speculation. In any case matter and anti-matter are indistinguishable, and their chemistry is identical.

Thus modern astronomy has shown, in a manner that leaves little room for doubt, that chemistry is a *universal* science. So then, if there is life elsewhere than on our earth, we must conclude that the living organisms on far distant planets are built up out of the same elements as those with which we are already familiar.

Starting with this as a premise, it will now be possible to discuss, on a factual basis, the possibility that life may adapt itself to conditions not found on earth.

REQUIREMENTS OF LIFE: ORGANIZATION

First of all, then, what does life involve? At this point we must confine our reasoning to the consideration of a particular kind of life—the life of animate matter. It is conceivable that fully alive immaterial beings exist—discarnate spirits, ghosts, angels, their kith and kin. If so, their existence is in no way bound up with chemistry. Obviously we cannot use science to rule out the possibility that angels inhabit the sun or that devils live in the middle of the earth. Our discussion, if it is to be based upon scientific knowledge at all, must be concerned only with living organisms that are constructed out of matter.

To continue, then, the first and most obvious requirement in living matter is that it should be *organized*. It matters not how different celestial living organisms may be from the living creatures we know on earth; if they are living in any sense they must be organized, that is to say, they must consist of parts that are held together in such a way that they can fulfil functions.

TEMPERATURE: AN UPPER LIMIT

If matter is to be organized, it is essential that chemical atoms should become firmly joined to one another, thus yielding structures that possess strength. Under what conditions, then, do atoms link together? This is a question that can be answered directly by appeal to experiment. It is found that while a majority of atoms will link together readily enough at the temperatures with which we are most familiar—say from room temperature up to that of a rather cool flame—combinations of all of them break to pieces at higher temperatures. Indeed, at a few thousand degrees Centigrade, all compounds decompose while solid elements melt and then become vapours, showing that even the forces which hold metals together can no longer do so when the temperature is very high. True, a few elements such as carbon and tungsten can withstand higher temperatures than the rest, but the time soon comes when these, too, become formless vapours.

The simplest combinations contain two atoms only, and a few of such compounds are just capable of existing in some of the cooler stars (they appear first in G and K-type stars and become more marked in the M, N, R and S-types) and, more rarely, in sunspots. A few very simple compounds (CN and CH) occur also in interstellar space. They can be identified by the spectral bands to which they give rise. But it is rare for more than two atoms to be found joined together in this way—even water containing three atoms (H_2O) is usually incapable of existence, though a combination (HO) of one hydrogen and one oxygen atom occurs. However, both water and carbon dioxide are found occasionally on very cool stars.

In considering these compounds, it must be borne in mind that the atoms do not necessarily stay joined to one another for very long. If they remain combined for a few millionths of a second a spectrum will be obtained. Perhaps the most stable of the stellar compounds do not exist for more than a small fraction of a second.

There is, then, a temperature limit above which chemical compounds cannot exist, and this is the temperature—say 2,000-4,000° C.—at the surface of the cooler stars. Here groups of two or three atoms become linked together for short intervals of time, but any more complex organization is out of the question. Above this temperature atoms cannot combine at all. Indeed, the atoms themselves then begin to break up, splitting off electrons in varying numbers until, finally, only their positive cores are left behind.

Coming down the temperature scale, we find that more complicated compounds, the molecules of which are still far too small to be of any service to organized living matter, can occasionally exist at a dull red heat. It is only in recent years that a few chemical substances (such as the metallic phthalocyanines and certain compounds of fluorine) of moderate complexity have been isolated which are not broken up at once by such temperatures. But even these are not stable at a red heat for any length of time, and they are of an unusually stable type.

From these facts only one conclusion can be drawn. Life is impossible at any temperature above, say, 500° or 600° C., and it would be hard enough to conceive of its possibility even at this temperature.

From this conclusion there is no escape. Already we know something about all the elements in the periodic table—there is no chance whatever of an hitherto unknown element being involved in living matter in other parts of the universe. Nor is there any reasonable possibility that matter can form organizations in the heavens that it cannot form on earth—for chemistry is universal, it is not merely peculiar to our earth.

It is true, of course, that under the enormous pressures and temperatures in the interior of the stars, matter must exist in unfamiliar forms. But here the atoms are mere positive charges stripped of their electrons (a state of matter known as *plasma*) and atomic cores do not join up to form stable organized structures.

When we consider the temperature of the universe, taken as a whole, a striking fact emerges. Until recently it was supposed that practically all the matter of the universe was concentrated in stars or, if not in stars, in whirling masses of gas out of which stars were in the process of condensing. Nowadays, however, the view is gaining ground among astronomers that a large fraction—perhaps 50 per cent, perhaps even 90 per cent—of cosmic matter is not in stars at all but distributed as clouds in interstellar space. Such clouds are visible in many parts of the heavens—the best known being that in the Horse Head nebula in Orion, the curious shape of which is undoubtedly due to the fact that much of the nebula is obscured by cloud. A new technique in radio-astronomy also makes is possible to map the positions of these hydrogen clouds in our own galaxy. In such clouds the pressures are exceedingly low while the temperatures cannot be far removed from the absolute zero. In any case, whatever the precise proportion of matter that exists in the form of clouds, it is clear that the vast bulk of the matter in the universe is either at a very high temperature—up to forty million or so degrees Centigrade in the centre of the stars, or else at very low temperatures near absolute zero.[1]

TEMPERATURE: A LOWER LIMIT

We have discussed the absolute upper limit of temperature at which organized matter can exist. But what about the lower limit? Complex organization can exist readily enough at low temperatures. Thus, the spores of some bacilli can be kept at the temperature of liquid air for months without being killed. Is it unreasonable then, to suppose that some living organisms, in other parts of the universe, may adapt themselves to live at temperatures near the absolute zero?

If life required the presence of organized matter only, this speculation would appear to be reasonable enough. But life normally involves chemical reactions also. If an animal is to move, to eat, to reproduce, to resist infection or to repair its tissues, chemical reactions must take place in its body. And it is hardly possible to imagine any form of life—or, at least of *conscious* life —which performs none of these functions. Indeed, such life, if it exists at all, would hardly be of much interest.

In the nineteenth century, it was supposed that chemical reactions take place whenever atoms hit one another. According to this view, a lowering of the temperature simply means that chemical reactions will take place less rapidly than before. Now, even at the temperature of liquid air, atoms collide about a third as frequently as at ordinary temperatures. So it was little suspected that chemical reactions would be slowed down by low temperatures to anything more than a moderate extent. This being so, it appeared reasonable to suppose that life might adapt itself, if necessary, to exceedingly low temperatures when the life-processes might, perhaps, be somewhat slowed down, but by no means stopped.

Developments in chemistry, which belong in the main to our

---

[1] It should, perhaps, be pointed out that the word "temperature" as applied to a rarefied gas is ambiguous. We may (a) measure the temperature which a thermometer, placed in the gas, would finally acquire, or (b) we may calculate the temperature from our knowledge of the average energy of the atoms present. Using the first definition, the temperature of interstellar matter comes out at only a few degrees above absolute zero, but, using the second, it is many thousands of degrees. The difference is due to the fact that a thermometer, placed in space, will radiate its heat.

own century, radically undermined these views. Measurements showed that with practically all chemical reactions, a fall in temperature of a few degrees does not lower the velocity of the change by the mere 1 per cent or so expected, but produces an *enormous* fall off in the rate. (Thus a fall in temperature of ten degrees usually reduces the rate to a half or a third of what it was before. Sometimes the reduction is much greater than this. Everyone knows that it is hard to cook eggs on mountain tops. A fall in temperature of 10° C. slows down the rate of cooking of the white of egg by about a thousandfold!)

For a long time this extraordinary sensitivity of the rate of chemical change to alterations in temperature remained a baffling mystery. At last, however, the puzzle was solved. Calculations show that in ordinary chemical changes only a very minute fraction of the atoms or molecules which strike one another actually react at all—the vast majority simply rebound unaltered. But, when the temperature changes, the magnitude of this small fraction changes greatly. Suffice it to say that the atoms or molecules which react possess more than a certain minimum of energy.[1] And at very low temperatures reactions stop, since none of the atoms possess the energy required. Indeed, at liquid air temperatures one might have to wait for thousands or millions of years before a *single* atom, by chance, possessed enough energy to enable it to react. In brief, reactions are completely stopped by very low temperatures, although the atoms go on colliding much the same as before, though rather less frequently.

Experiments have shown that practically all reactions become vanishingly slow if the temperature is lowered to −50 or −100° C. At liquid air temperature—still very high compared with the temperature of most of the matter in space—only a very few reactions take place at all and these all involve the exceedingly active element fluorine in its free state.

---

[1] It does not follow that all which possess this energy will, in fact, react—another factor, connected with entropy, may reduce the lucky ones to one in a million of these. The analogy of hopping insects (see p. 27) affords a tolerably accurate picture of the situation. To get from one partition of a box to the other the individual insects must (1) have enough energy to hop over any barrier there may be between the compartments and (2) they must hop in the right direction.

LIFE'S TEMPERATURE RANGE

Thus chemical reactions being essential to living organisms, it follows that life can never adapt itself either to very high or very low temperatures. This does not, of course, mean that very low temperatures will necessarily kill all living matter—we know, as a matter of fact, that lower and sometimes even higher forms of life can survive them. But it does mean that living organisms can only exist in a state of suspense, without movement, without breathing, without feeding, and without propagating their species under such conditions. Moreover, there is good evidence to show that seeds and spores cannot retain the spark of life for ever in this condition.

We must conclude that life can only acclimatize itself to a very limited range of temperature. On the one hand chemical atoms cannot remain combined if the temperature is very high, while, on the other, the chemical reactions essential to life cannot take place if the temperature is very low.

The days when men were free to imagine strange monsters climbing the solar prominences, building houses in the sunspots, inhabiting interstellar space or flourishing in the icy cold regions of the moon and outer planets are gone for ever. "Varieties of creatures" there may certainly be in nature, but the varieties are not so strange and unearthly as was once supposed.

CHAPTER V

PLANETARY INHABITANTS?

IN the preceding chapters, we have told the story of man's speculations about his place in the universe. Is he alone—suspended on a little world in a vast immensity of space—or is it possible that there are other inhabited worlds dotted endlessly throughout the sky? That is the question which has always been of such absorbing interest. But in the past the will to believe, or to disbelieve, has influenced human judgement on this matter far more than any facts which might have been adduced one way or the other. Today, however, modern science is providing a certain bedrock of fact—some part of which we have already investigated in the preceding chapter. In the light of present scientific knowledge we may now proceed to inquire whether life is to be found on any of the other bodies in our own solar system.

THE MOON

First of all we may consider the moon, our nearest neighbour in space. Calculation shows that a body of so small a size cannot possess an atmosphere—for the gravitational attraction is insufficient to retain one. The few stray atoms, formed by radioactive decay from the rocks, soon wander off into space, after "bouncing" perhaps two or three times on the lunar surface.

Calculation agrees well with the results of direct observation. If the moon possessed an atmosphere it would bend the sun's rays during an eclipse and this would give rise to a bright ring of light around the edge of the satellite. Nothing of this kind has ever been observed, however, for the edge of the moon always presents a sharp outline. Similarly, radio waves, coming from distant radio stars, are shut off sharply when the moon comes between these stars and ourselves.

Possessing virtually no atmosphere, the moon of course has no water. Direct observation with telescopes shows clearly enough that it has no form of vegetation—even quite small patches of vegetation would be readily visible through large telescopes. Radio waves, directed at the moon, bounce back as if from a polished mirror! Apart from craters its surface is flat and smooth—no gentle slopes, no stones and boulders—just a featureless wilderness of dust, sand and possibly small pebbles. This covering has little power to retain heat—during the short period of the eclipse of the moon, temperature drops of over 200° C. have been measured (117° C. down to −101° C.). Here and there outgrowths of mineral deposits can be discerned—in one spot the yellow colour of sulphur is said to be visible. Widely dispersed over much of the moon's surface, too, are the innumerable craters— varying in size from a few yards to tens of miles across—which were possibly formed in prehistoric ages when meteorites came crashing down from the skies. Gravity was small, and shining fragments, either of metal or of spheres of glass-like marbles, which spattered in all directions when they struck the satellite—fragments which on earth would get covered up or removed within a very short period—are still to be seen like great starfishes emanating from some of the craters of the moon.

These facts are sufficient to show that the moon cannot support life in any form. Exceedingly severe cold over the whole of its surface, due to the absence of an atmosphere, together with the absence of water which, as we shall presently see, is essential for life, show clearly enough that the moon's surface is no abode for living organisms. The first of the intrepid rocketeers to visit our satellite will certainly have no picnic.

These conclusions are in remarkable contrast to the views that used to be entertained, even as late as the nineteenth century. Sir William Herschel claimed to have seen up to 150 active volcanoes on the moon. Later W. H. Pickering was quite certain that he could discern lunar vegetation, hoar-frost and snow. Even today such views are revived from time to time. Charles Fort, for instance, in his amazing book *New Lands* (1923), declares that there are canals on the moon!

OUTER PLANETS

Leaving the moon, we may now consider the planets, starting with the outermost and working inwards towards the sun.

Very little was known about the outer planets until recent years. Pluto is very small—much smaller than the earth—and, being the farthest from the sun, must be the coldest of all. Little is known about Neptune and Uranus. Both appear to be covered with clouds —consisting, perhaps, of solid nitrogen or ammonia, and it seems certain that little if any light from the sun can penetrate to the surface of these planets. Measurement of the temperature of Uranus (worked out from the heat it radiates to the earth) show that it cannot be hotter than $-185°$ C., while calculation based on its distance from the sun gives the temperature $-212°$ C.

JUPITER AND SATURN

Saturn and Jupiter are also intensely cold, though they seem to be the scenes of vigorous activity at times. Their surface temperatures lie at about $-100°$ to $-150°$ C.

It seems that Jupiter, at all events, is still radiating an appreciable amount of its original heat, for it is apparently not as cold as it would be if the sun were its only source of heat.

For a long time it was uncertain whether Jupiter and Saturn possessed atmospheres. Then it was discovered that the sun's light, reflected from these planets, was deficient in the orange and green parts of the spectrum. For some time the meaning of this fact remained a mystery, for the spectral bands in question could not be obtained with any known gas in the laboratory. This was not altogether surprising; light reflected from a large planet may travel through hundreds of miles of atmosphere and it is difficult to experiment with tubes of this length in the laboratory! But in 1932 it was at last shown that the bands were due to the gases methane and ammonia, a result which has been several times confirmed by later workers.

The bands due to methane have been found with increasing intensity in the spectra of Saturn, Uranus and Neptune, but bands due to other simple hydrocarbons, such as ethane, are absent. On Jupiter there is at least enough methane to cover it to a thickness of half a mile, supposing it were measured at the ordinary barometric pressure of our own atmosphere. The amount of ammonia, on the other hand, corresponds only to a thickness of about thirty feet. On Neptune the ammonia has probably all become frozen, but the methane has increased to the equivalent of a thickness of twenty-five miles.

Jupiter and Saturn are both covered with "cloud". But this "cloud" possibly consists of crystals of frozen ammonia. Very occasionally the crystals appear to be contaminated with metallic compounds which gives rise to beautiful colour effects—particularly reds and blues. It is supposed that the famous red spots which appeared on Jupiter in the seventeenth and nineteenth centuries, were formed in this way.[1]

On Jupiter, the clouds of frozen ammonia appear to be suspended in an atmosphere which—on account of something akin to trade winds—gives rise to a peculiar streaky appearance. Though the atmosphere contains methane, hydrogen and helium may also be present in great quantities. Since these planets are completely obscured by clouds, we do not know the state of the surface below. There may be oceans of liquid gases resting upon an enormous thickness of ice. Of this, of course, we cannot be certain, but since the major planets are not nearly as massive as we should expect them to be, were they made chiefly of materials similar to those that form our own earth, it seems necessary to suppose that they are made of very light forms of matter.

Jupiter has eleven moons and Saturn nine but most of these are very small. The largest of them all is Titan, which belongs to Saturn. This is comparable in size with our own moon—indeed, it is somewhat larger. It is the only satellite in the entire solar system to possess an atmosphere and it has been found that this atmosphere contains methane and ammonia—the same as in the parent planet. Owing to the extremely low temperature—Titan only receives about 1 per cent of the radiation received by our moon—gases are retained despite the low gravitational attraction.

The low temperatures of all these planets and their satellites, together with the unfavourable atmospheric conditions, make it almost impossible to believe that they contain living organisms. But the chances seem more favourable on the planets nearer the sun.

[1] Metals such as sodium and calcium dissolve in liquid ammonia to give highly coloured solutions—blue and red.

THE PLANET MARS: ITS SURFACE

The next planet, in order, is Mars. This is smaller than the earth in size—its surface area being about one quarter of the earth's. The average temperature is close to that of the earth, though a little lower; the length of its day is about the same as ours, though the year is nearly twice as long. It has two small moons, Phobos and Demos.

Mars is remarkable in many ways and it is generally agreed that if there is life anywhere in the solar system, other than on our earth, it must be there. But the conditions are much less favourable than they are on our own planet. Thus, the temperature changes on the surface of the planet are excessive. Some 2,000 measurements made in 1953 gave a mean range of $-47°$ to $+21°$ C. for the night and day temperatures, but temperatures as low as $-80°$ C. have been recorded. Only very few forms of life would be able to withstand frosts of such a magnitude. The reason for this tremendous fall in temperature is doubtless connected with the scarcity of water—for Mars appears to possess no seas or large inland lakes. On earth it is the enormous heat-retaining capacity of water which provides us with so even a temperature.

Mars is not wholly devoid of water, for polar caps are seen to come and go with the seasons. The enormous rapidity with which they do so, however, shows that there is no abundant water supply, even at the white-capped poles. Indeed, assuming that the "snow-caps" do, in fact, consist of snow or hoar-frost, calculations have shown that this cannot be more than a few inches in thickness.

Occasionally white clouds have been reported on Mars, but they are uncommon. On the other hand huge clouds of yellowish dust—best seen in infra-red light—make their appearance at times—and move across the face of the planet as if moved by violent winds. For a time the hue of Mars as a whole will change. This is evidence, not only that water is very scarce, but that much at least of the planet is covered by dry dust—as difficult an environment for living organisms as an arid desert.

Large areas of the planet are coloured red and all are agreed that these are deserts. But there are also darker areas which look bluish-green and the depth and hue of this colour changes with the seasons. What are they? Areas of primitive vegetation—akin to certain lichens and mosses found on high mountains? So many believe. Russian workers claim that the spectrum of the light from these areas (the spectrum is quite unlike that of the chlorophyll of green plants) resembles that from the Siberian wastes viewed at a great distance. A famous Russian professor grows lichens and liverworts in the Atlai mountains and claims to be studying "astrobotanical vegetation". An American worker claims that the resonant frequency of the C–H bond can be discerned in the spectrum, again suggesting vegetation.

More prosaic possibilities cannot be discounted. According to one view powdered rock, in the low-lying areas, containing bluish-green, slightly oxidized iron ore, deepens in colour as it becomes moist at the time of the disappearance of the polar caps. An interesting view (McLaughlin, 1955) is that there are a few active volcanoes on the planet. At certain seasons the monsoon winds spread a cloud of fresh greenish ash over the ground. It is claimed that the areas of seasonal variation always follow the prevailing winds and that the amount of dust shot up is comparable in amount with that ejected by earthly volcanoes.

The red colour of so much of the planet is usually assumed to mean that iron—in the form of oxide—has been oxidized, at least superficially, by free oxygen or ozone. If this be so, it is well to remember that during the early stages of the oxidation of iron oxides, first pale and then dark green intermediates are formed. It is only to be expected that oxidation would have been much more complete in certain areas—those where moisture was abundant—than in others. And in an oxygen-starved atmosphere volcanic dust would almost certainly be greenish.

MARTIAN ATMOSPHERE

This leads us to a consideration of the atmosphere of Mars. The planet is known to have a fairly dense atmosphere but its exact nature has not been determined. Water vapour, as we have seen, is evidently present in traces—and its presence has been confirmed spectroscopically. Nitrogen may be present in large amounts but there is no known way of detecting its presence. Carbon dioxide has been detected in quantity comparable to that on earth.

Interest naturally centres chiefly round the question of oxygen. As we have seen, the redness of the rocks strongly suggests the presence of this element and, until recent decades, it was universally supposed to be present.

The first rough observations before the First World War seemed to confirm this belief and it was estimated that the amount of oxygen present was about 15 per cent of that on the earth. But later observation has shown that this result was wrong, and it is now certain that if there is any oxygen present it is less than one-thousandth of that on the earth.

The absence of oxygen raises a considerable difficulty for the vegetation theory. If vegetation is so abundant that vast seasonal changes, affecting a large proportion of the area of the planet, are easily visible from our earth, we should certainly expect oxygen to be abundant. It is useless to urge that, perhaps, the vegetation is of a kind different from that with which we are familiar, a kind that does not generate oxygen gas—for in that case, the whole argument based upon the resemblance between the planet's greenish colour and the colour of earthly plants is valueless.

Unfortunately the subject is befogged by emotional issues. The disagreement that existed between Sir Harold Spencer Jones and Sir James Jeans—both men of the highest eminence—illustrates this point well. In print, Jones often took it for granted that the existence of plant life on Mars had been proved. The red colour of the planet, he said, was a convincing argument for the presence of oxygen, at least at some period of the planet's history, and he concluded "the presence of free oxygen almost certainly demands the presence of vegetation"; and again, it is "now reasonably certain, that there is vegetation . . . The evidence of plant life of some sort on Mars is very reassuring for those who believe that, wherever in the universe conditions suitable for life prevail, there life will somehow come into existence. It makes it difficult to continue to believe that life on the earth is the result of some special unique act of creation."[1]

However, as Jeans quickly pointed out, these dogmatic statements by Spencer Jones really assumed what the latter wished to prove: namely that life will arise whenever the conditions are favourable and, added Jeans, "others may prefer to make the opposite assumption."

[1] *Life on Other Worlds*, 1940, p. 207, and *Times*, July 29, 1939. No such dogmatic statements occur in his less popular writings. For the review by J. H. Jeans see *Nature*, 1940, **146**, 211 ff.

In the opinion of Sir James Jeans the facts of astronomy gave no ground whatever for the view that plant life is present on Mars—rather the reverse.

"It is surely going too far to say that 'the colour of the surface of Mars provides sure evidence of the presence of free oxygen, at any rate in the past' and to continue 'the presence of free oxygen almost certainly demands the existence of vegetation'. Surely the observations are most simply explained by supposing that the free oxygen which came from the sun has all, or nearly all, been absorbed by the rocks; the question of vegetation does not come in at all, except that if there were abundant vegetation we should expect to find abundant free oxygen in the atmosphere which we emphatically do not." As for the seasonal colour changes, Jeans remarks, "Spencer Jones rejects Arrhenius's suggestion that the areas in question may be covered with soluble or hygroscopic salts that change their colour in rainy weather. He might have added that Lyot's recent careful studies of the reflecting and polarizing qualities of the surface of Mars seem to indicate that this consists of volcanic ash—like the moon."

Before leaving this subject one other point may be mentioned. Not only may the sun have provided Mars, in addition to the other planets, with an excess of oxygen when they were first formed, but an excess of oxygen must have been present for a totally different reason. If there is water on a planet, it will be decomposed rapidly by the sun's intense ultra-violet light, to give oxygen and hydrogen. Molecules of hydrogen, being very light, must soon escape into space leaving the heavier oxygen held fast by the planet's gravity. Indeed, recent exploration by rockets, has shown that our earth is surrounded by a "geocorona" of hydrogen atoms which are even now escaping into space, and the loss of hydrogen may perhaps have depressed the level of the oceans in recent geological time. In the early history of the planet Mars, therefore, when water was more abundant than it is today, there must have been more than ample oxygen to redden the rocks by oxidation.

LIFE ON MARS?

Thus the present state of our knowledge gives little warrant for the belief that there is life on Mars—certainly not life of an advanced kind and probably not even of a lowly vegetable kind.

This conclusion is in marked contrast to the views that were held until well into the present century. It was once supposed that the surface of the planet was covered with canals, running in straight lines for thousands of miles. An elaborate theory was built up by Lowell according to which the Martians, being short of water, built these canals to irrigate their planets.[1] Today, it is generally believed that practically all the minute details of these canals are non-existent, as they have tended to disappear when looked for through the more powerful telescopes now available. Nevertheless, straight or nearly straight lines can still be discerned, though the term "canals" is scarcely warrantable. Their nature is unknown—one suggestion is that they represent the valleys of ancient rivers in which light mists now occasionally collect. It is not at all certain that the lines are really continuous—the eye tends to join a number of points together by imaginary lines. In any case, lines are probably not an unusual feature in astronomical geography—they are well represented in the moon (e.g. a straight gorge, six miles wide and seventy-five miles long in the mountains which border *Mare Imbrium*), but here no one calls them "canals".

In view of the relative absence of water, the huge temperature fluctuations and, above all, the absence of oxygen, higher if not lower forms of life are certainly absent.[2]

VENUS

The next planet to Mars is the earth. After that comes Venus which, like Mars, has long been looked upon as a possible abode of life.

The surface of Venus is invisible, the planet being always covered completely with cloud. The planet emits bursts of radio waves, due perhaps to storms, which apparently escape into space through a "hole" in the ions which cover its surface. Observing

[1] A modern variant of these sensationalist views has recently been proposed and is now (1959) in vogue in some quarters. It is claimed that the moons of Mars are hollow spheres, made of steel a few inches thick, manufactured by extinct Martians at a remote epoch in time.

[2] It is reported (*Science*, 1960, **131**, 1819) that the sun's light, reflected from Mars, shows detailed agreement over the whole visible range with the absorption spectrum of nitrogen dioxide, NO_2, which gas is evidently present in considerable quantity. This red gas may be partly or wholly responsible for the colour of the planet and perhaps for the seasonal changes also. With moisture the gas gives nitric acid (together with nitrous acid) and its presence in all save the minutest traces would certainly make life impossible.

the way these "bursts" come and go has led (1956) to the conclusion that the length of the planet's day is twenty-two hours of
our time—not a few weeks as had previously been supposed.

The atmosphere contains carbon dioxide in enormous quantity—
there is about twice as much of this gas as there is of oxygen on
earth. In 1956 a Russian worker claimed to detect bands due to
nitrogen in the faint natural glow of the planet's atmosphere.
Water has not as yet been found but, as the temperature at the
upper surface of the clouds is only −39° C., it is clear that all the
water must have frozen out and so its vapour would be hard to
detect. As with Mars there is no oxygen: a thousandth part of
that present on earth would be detectable.

The cloud surface is yellowish and ultra-violet light shows bands
of light and dark clouds in violent motion at a lower level. The
clouds are usually supposed to consist of dust, suggesting that the
entire surface of the planet is a waterless desert, black as night since
the sun's rays never penetrate the cloud, and exceedingly hot too—
for not only is the planet nearer the Sun than Earth, but its temperature is kept high by the "greenhouse" effect of carbon dioxide.
Just possibly, however, the clouds are due to water (Whipple,
1957). If so, the planet must be covered completely with a hot
ocean probably near boiling-point. No land masses can arise
from the ocean to form continents as on earth—for wet rocks
exposed to carbon dioxide would soon absorb the gas and form
carbonates.

Desert or ocean, the outcome is the same. No oxygen; and so, no
vegetation and no photosynthesis. All seem agreed that life is
precluded in such conditions which would be aggravated by
the high temperature. Absence of water would also preclude life
and, if water is present, absence of continents would preclude
land life.

Before life arrived on earth, our own atmosphere may have been
very similar to that of Venus. Carbon dioxide was present in
gigantic quantities but oxygen was scarce. Specimens of this early
atmosphere (from which, however, oxygen may have been removed
by chemical reaction) may have been preserved for us in the bubbles
occluded in some volcanic rocks, and they possibly serve to
verify the truth of these statements. But when once life came the
carbon dioxide was rapidly used up and replaced by oxygen. Thus

the present atmosphere of Venus is again strong evidence that life is absent.[1]

MERCURY

With regard to Mercury, the last of the planets, little needs to be said. All the indications show that its surface is similar to that of the moon, save that it is much hotter—in fact, the temperature of the rocks on the side which faces the sun is about that of molten zinc.

Mercury possesses no water and no atmosphere. If ever it had either of these, they must have disappeared long ago. The gravitational attraction of this small planet is quite insufficient to prevent light molecules escaping into space. (It is considered possible by some astronomers that Mercury may still retain an exceedingly tenuous atmosphere of heavy gases.)

In addition to the planets we have mentioned there are thousands of minor planets, or asteroids (of which *Ceres*, the largest, is 500 miles across) and also a few satellites of considerable size. On all of them, however, the physical conditions are too unfavourable for life to be possible.

DIFFERENCE FROM OLDER VIEWS

It is hardly possible to exaggerate the difference between the views that are now held by astronomers and those that were once held to be plausible. At one time even the comets—mere collections of stones and rarefied gases, as we now know them to be—were considered to be probable abodes of life. Maupertuis thought they were inhabited by a race of men, and in their phosphorescent tails he saw a train of dazzling jewels. In his *Lettre sur la Comète* (1752) he pictures a collision between a comet and the earth: "We should perhaps be much surprised to find that the remains of those bodies which we despise are formed of gold or diamonds; but which would be the more surprised of the two, ourselves or the inhabitants whom the comet would land upon earth?"

The days when every intelligent man and woman was forced, if

---

[1] It is reported (Drake, 1960) that radio waves emitted by the planet indicate an average surface temperature of well over 300° C., indicating that the conditions are those of a desert.

he thought at all, to believe that space was populated with worlds are gone for ever. Detailed knowledge of the skies does not extend outside our own solar system, but this contains a great assortment of heavenly bodies. Yet on all of them, save on our own earth, the conditions are inhospitable to life. We are alone. Evidently, it is no usual thing for a planet to be habitable. In the vast spaces of the heavens there may, perhaps, be other suns accompanied by planets comparable to those with which we are familiar—though evidence on this point is lacking. But even if this proved to be so, these planets might well be as uninhabited as are all save one of the bodies in our solar system. Who can tell?

There is the time factor to consider too. Our earth has circled around the sun for perhaps a thousand million times since life started, but civilized thinking man has not been here for more than a fifty-thousandth part of this time—the equivalent of one page only in a library of perhaps 500–1,000 books telling the story of life on Earth. (Count the hominids of half a million years ago, and even then it is but a page in a good-sized volume.) If we live on an unusual planet, we live also in an unusual epoch of that planet. Can we say that for every hundred thousand planets like ours, only two or three are likely to be inhabited with thinking creatures?

CHAPTER VI

A PLANET'S BLUE-PRINT

WE have noted that our earth is the only planet in the solar system on the surface of which living organisms—except, conceivably, those of a very low degree of complexity—can flourish. What, then, are the peculiar features of the earth which make it so well suited as an abode of life?

In order to discuss this question concretely, we shall indulge, first of all, in a fantasy. Let us imagine ourselves in the shoes of a junior god or demiurge who has been given the task of planning an abode for life. And let us suppose that we have been told to attend to the various physical factors which will need attention.

First of all there is the maintenance of an approximately constant temperature. We have already noted that life on earth is only possible because the earth's orbit lies in the "temperate zone" of the solar system. It will be necessary, therefore, to arrange for our imaginary planet to be placed at the correct average distance from a suitable star. The star must, of course, be one which shines steadily, not one of the variable kind. It must not be a binary star system either, for a planet would be hard put to it to maintain an even temperature if its two suns were for ever gyrating about one another! But the selection of a suitable star should offer no great difficulty.

Next, we shall have to arrange matters so that the planet's orbit is circular, or at least very nearly so. It seems likely that, in whatever way we may bring our solar system into existence, our planet will, at first, move in a highly eccentric orbit. But if, instead of one planet, we have several and allow them to rotate round the star for a long time, they will react upon one another—perhaps, with occasional collisions—in such a manner that they will eventually move in circles after which there will be little more interference. If our planet should be destroyed by an unlucky collision with one of its neighbours before its orbit has settled down, we may have to start again. But there is a reasonable hope that it will· survive unharmed.

It will be necessary for the intensity of radioactivity to be very low—the delicate and complex molecules of which living matter is composed are soon destroyed by the shower of high-speed electrons, *alpha*-particles and X-rays emitted by the less stable elements. Both the expansion of the universe in its early stages and the explosion of a *nova* or *super-nova* are associated with radioactive matter in great abundance. If planets result from such processes it will, then, on this account also, be necessary to wait a thousand million years or more for the planet to "cool off".

Next, in order to even out its temperature as much as possible, we must make sure that the planet rotates fairly rapidly. And this rotation must take place in the right plane—otherwise we may bathe one pole in months of sunshine while the other remains in seasonal darkness. But it will help very greatly if the axis of rotation is not at right angles to the plane of rotation around the sun—for in this way seasonable variations of temperature could be secured and a much larger proportion of the planet's surface will become habitable.

Even so, the temperature variations will be enormous. We might hope to equalize them by causing the planet to rotate very rapidly but to this there is the serious objection that the centrifugal forces set up will lower the planet's stability. Some other way of keeping the planet at a constant temperature must be devised.

NEED FOR WATER

A way out of the difficulty would be to find a substance with a very high capacity for heat. If it were a solid—a rock, for instance —its conductivity would have to be high, so that the heat would rapidly penetrate into the deeper layers. However, since no such solid exists, a liquid would have to be chosen instead—the deeper layers of a clear liquid can be warmed by radiation and cooled by convection. But it will be necessary for our liquid, which would receive warmth in the day and retain it at night, to be present in enormous quantities, covering a large fraction of the planet's surface.

Of all the possible liquids which could be used for this purpose, there is no doubt that water is the most suitable. It has practically the highest heat capacity of any known substance and possesses numerous other advantages which, though highly beneficial to life, may not always be absolutely necessary for its existence.

The use of water would also open up the possibility of ensuring a relatively constant temperature in another way. If the heat from the star became at any time too intense, it would warm the surface of the water and cause extensive evaporation. The vapour would rise and become cooled, so making cloud. This cloud would then reflect the sun's rays back into space, so protecting the oceans and land below. On the other hand if, at any time, the temperature became too low, clouds would tend to disappear, and the sun's rays would be able once more to shine upon the surface of the planet. In this way, the use of water would help to maintain a fairly constant temperature at the planet's surface. Clouds would also be of great importance in helping to distribute the heat. For the heat absorbed by the surface of the water in the process of evaporation would be given up once more when the water-vapour condensed to give cloud or rain. Since vapours would easily travel great distances at considerable speeds, this would enable the heat received from the star to be more fairly shared over the planet's surface.

We shall, therefore, be well advised to arrange for the production of clouds on our hypothetical planet. Now modern research shows that water-vapour will not, of itself, produce clouds at all readily. Nuclei must be provided on which the water can condense. Stray electric charges (from cosmic rays or radioactive matter) cannot provide adequate nuclei and will not, indeed, produce any clouds at all except when the degree of supersaturation becomes exceedingly high. Continuous outbursts from large numbers of volcanoes might provide nuclei in sufficient numbers—but if volcanoes were common, conditions on the planet would not be peaceful! Meteoric dust might work well enough (as in fact, according to a recent theory, it does) but its availability is probably too spasmodic to prove generally useful.

SALTS

The difficulty might be overcome by dissolving salts, in huge quantities, in the water of the ocean. Winds would blow the waves against a thousand shores and minute droplets of water would evaporate into the air, leaving little specks of salt which would be

carried far and wide by winds. In this way nuclei for the formation of rain could be made generally available over the surface of
the planet. Evidently we must arrange for vast quantities of salt to
become dissolved in our ocean water. We might do this by making
our sea acid, at least in its early ages, so that it could extract metals
from the rocks with which it was in contact. But, however we set
about the matter, we should be faced by a new difficulty. In whatever way we cause our sea to be made salt, it seems inevitable that
the water would not only dissolve non-poisonous salts, such as the
chlorides of sodium and magnesium, from the rocks, but that the
salts of other metals also would accumulate in large amount. Now
some of these, particularly those of the elements arsenic, mercury
and lead, are exceedingly poisonous. The reason for this lies, apparently, in the fact that the atoms of these metals attach themselves
strongly to sulphur. Now living organisms depend upon the
presence of certain sulphur compounds (such as cysteine, gluta-
thione and lipoic acid) which are made and unmade in the reversible
processes in the body. When, therefore, these metals are present,
fundamental mechanisms upon which life depends are prevented
from operating. It seems certain, therefore, that if we desired our
planet to support life—at all events, the kind of life with which we
are familiar—it would be necessary to prevent the poisoning of all
the water on the globe! So we are faced with the formidable
problem of how to remove poisonous metals from the sea and yet
to leave the harmless ones. By no means an easy problem! (Later
we shall turn to see how the problem has actually been solved in
nature.)

SEA AND LAND

Leaving aside this difficulty, let us decide, then, that a large part
of the surface of our planet shall be covered by an ocean of sea
water containing salt. But this poses yet another formidable
problem. How can we ensure that there shall be land? No matter
by what natural means we choose to bring our planet into existence,
the planet will certainly take the shape of a sphere. This will
probably mean that the waters will cover it uniformly and, if so,
perhaps we shall have to be content with marine life only.

Perhaps the difficulty is not quite so great as we have represented
it. Here and there, after the lapse of ages, mountain ranges might

rise up, making chains of small islands in our world-wide ocean. Volcanoes, too, might poke their heads through the watery waste. But islands thus formed will tend to lie only along a few geological fault-lines, and will not be very permanent.

The vast bulk of the planet will remain for ever covered by the sea—without continents or large islands and, probably, without land life.

It is not at all easy to think of a simple plan for avoiding this difficulty. When we turn to nature we find the bulk of the earth's surface is covered with water, but to our astonishment we also find that over one side of the earth vast continents have risen above the water-level, while on the other side of the earth there is an enormous ocean, the Pacific, covering a third of the earth's surface.

Such an arrangement is the last thing we should expect to find in a planet which has quietly cooled down from a molten state and then become covered with water. This situation seems to be unique in the solar system, as we have already noted. How it was accomplished we simply do not know—unless, indeed, the older view that the moon separated from the earth leaving a crater on one side is right after all.

PLANET'S SIZE

Many other matters, also, would require serious attention. We have taken it for granted that, if our planet possessed an ocean, the ocean would stay in place instead of quietly evaporating into space —as it may have done on Mars. Moreover, we have not yet considered the question of an atmosphere.

The presence of both water and an atmosphere demand, not merely that our planet must be stationed at a certain distance from a suitable star, but that it must be of a certain size. This necessity arises on account of the fact that the molecules of gases and vapours are in constant motion. At the "top" of the atmosphere some of them will, therefore, fly off into space unless the gravitational attraction of the planet is sufficiently great to pull them back again. Had the earth been as small as Mercury or the moon it would have been incapable of retaining either water or an atmosphere.

If, on the other hand, our planet is made too large its atmosphere will not be of the right kind. First of all, there will be too much water and, secondly, the gases helium and hydrogen will almost certainly be present in gigantic quantities. This can only mean that, as with the larger planets in our own solar system, there will be an abundance of reducing gases together with the poisonous gas ammonia. In addition, the resulting very thick atmosphere will probably shield the planet from the sun's rays.

It is not possible to say, for certain, what limits of tolerance we may allow. But they will probably be very small—perhaps only a few per cent. A much wider tolerance than this might be allowed if we were concerned only about retaining the right kind of atmosphere. But to ensure the right amount of water will be a much more critical matter. If, as seems likely, the water of an ocean must first of all be dissolved in molten rocks (see later, p. 88), then a doubling of the mass of the planet would mean that twice as much water as before would be available. But the surface of the planet would then be only 1·59 times as great as before, so that the average depth of the ocean would increase by about 26 per cent. Much less than this might entail the submergence of much of the continents.

SPECIFICATION FOR LIFE

Such are some of the points to which we shall need to give attention in order to proceed with our design. It is not unlikely that this is the first part of our story only and that, with fuller knowledge, many other matters, also, will have to be looked into. The star in our planetary system might have to be of a special kind, its position relative to the galaxy containing it might be a matter of importance, cosmic rays might be necessary for life—perhaps, for generating biological mutations—and so forth. Of these and other possible factors we know little or nothing but our present knowledge does indicate with some degree of certainty that it would be no easy task to draw up a complete specification of a planet on the surface of which living organisms might live. It hardly seems likely that all the requirements could ever be fulfilled by coincidence.

Our experiment in attempting to draw up a "blue-print" of a planet serves to emphasize a point which we might well have anticipated. Our planet has got to "work"—it has got to support life. Now our experience of matter goes to show that it is no easy thing to design things which work. The inventor is always confronted by a succession of difficulties—he constantly finds that some of his requirements are inconsistent with others and has to exercise his ingenuity to avoid difficulties and pitfalls. And our primary excursion into the art of planet-building has served to show that here, also, careful design is necessary and ingenuity must be exercised. Any planet will not do; the planet must conform to a very exacting specification.

In our own earth all the necessary conditions are evidently fulfilled. How did this happen? We may, of course, suppose that the earth was planned at the beginning of time by an Almighty Mind. But a sceptic might very well retort that it might just as well be due to coincidence, and as yet it would be difficult to answer him convincingly. After all, the mere fact that we are on this earth discussing its origin, shows that the earth is a fit place for us to live on. If it were not, we should not be here. Whenever a rare combination of circumstances combine to make a planet habitable, there, so we may be told, life is sure to develop. So an appearance of design may be of no significance at all.

After this short excursion into the realm of fancy we shall turn to consider how, in fact, the solar system and our own earth in particular may have reached their present state.

CHAPTER VII

EARTH'S BEGINNINGS

THE earth is evidently a remarkable place. But how did it come to exist? What light has science thrown on the subject?

The first scientist to direct attention to this question was Immanuel Swedenborg who developed his ideas in his *Principia,* published in 1734. Swedenborg declared that at one time what we now call the solar system consisted of a gaseous nebula in rapid rotation. As it cooled, it contracted and, turning faster and faster, it threw off a ring. This finally divided into several parts which in time became spherical and evolved into planets.[1]

Kant and later still Laplace developed the theory further. Laplace supposed that all the stars in the sky were rotating rapidly, throwing off rings of gaseous matter, which were condensing into planets.

Although Laplace was an able mathematician, he made no serious attempt to apply mathematics to this idea. Indeed, his exposition of it is to be found in a footnote in a popular book devoted to general science. Nevertheless, such was the respect in which Laplace was held, that his theory soon caught the imagination of laymen and scientists alike. There seems to be little doubt, however, that the chief reason for its sudden popularity lay in the fact that it was promulgated shortly after the French Revolution, when people were only too willing to accept uncritically a theory to which theologians were unlikely to give their approval!

Not until the present century was the nebula theory subjected to critical analysis. It appears that our sun has been shining, very much in its present state, for perhaps five or six thousand million years and yet it has shown no sign of producing more planets during this period. This makes it hard to understand why it should ever have done so in the first place. Mathematical analysis increases

---

[1] To this day spiritualists are apt to point with pride to the fact that Swedenborg, who claimed to hold converse with the spirits, was the first discoverer of the nebula theory. But in the light of present knowledge it certainly seems as if the spirits were misinformed!

difficulties yet further, for calculation shows that excessive rotation should cause stars to break up, but in doing so they should not produce rings at all, but should turn into binaries—binaries are common enough in the heavens. Again, even if rings *were* produced they would at once become dispersed and would not condense into planets.

Until about 1935 it was generally believed that the difficulties could be satisfactorily solved by a theory originally suggested by Buffon, and revived by Sir James Jeans. According to this, the solar system was formed as a result of a "near miss" between two stars which accidentally came very close to one another a long time ago. As a result of the encounter a gigantic tide was raised which, as it mounted higher and higher, eventually left the sun altogether. After this the two stars separated, leaving a great cigar-shaped mass of fiery matter suspended in the heavens.

By and by, as the great cigar cooled, it broke up into pieces. Numerous planets were formed—small ones both near and far from the sun, with large ones in the middle. These planets continued to revolve round the sun, as the great cigar had been revolving before them, and so our solar system came into being.

This theory was more successful, by far, than any previously suggested. But in 1935 Russell argued that, had the planets been formed in such a way, their angular momentum would have been much less than it is. This and other difficulties need not mean that the theory is wrong; a more complex one may be necessary. And Lyttleton soon showed that, for example, the Jeans theory could be adapted to start off with a binary star which suffered a near encounter with a third star, two of them being lost shortly afterwards. (More recently it has been shown that the cloud of ionized gas surrounding a star such as the sun will create magnetic fields which will slow down the rotation of the star, so that the angular momentum difficulty is no longer acute.)

If a theory can be maintained only by making it increasingly complex, it is natural to inquire whether other solutions to the problem in hand are possible. Over the past few decades astronomers have, accordingly, given much attention to new suggestions as to how the solar system might have come into existence.

In this connexion an important question arises—do other stars possess planets? If they do, then a collision theory is probably wrong, for stars are at such great distances apart that they have been compared to tiny midgets flying about—but flying *very* slowly —in a cave of Brobdingnagian dimensions. The chance that two will meet is lower than that of the proverbial finding of the needle in the haystack. But if planets are nowhere else to be found, or are very rare, then a collision theory seems reasonable enough.

The brightness of many stars changes slightly in a regular manner, with a period of a few years. This has been interpreted in Russia to indicate that these stars are surrounded by planetary systems, but the argument is weak. Even the radiation of the sun is by no means constant, quite apart from planets.

Long continued observation of the heavens has, however, revealed a few "planet-like" objects—or rather such objects have been postulated to account for perturbations in the stars. In the system 61 Cygni, however, there is believed to be an invisible body sixteen times as massive as Jupiter (i.e. 0·016 times the mass of the sun)—Jupiter being by far the largest planet in our solar system—while, in the star system 70 Ophiuchi there is one eight times as massive. These two are the smallest quasi-planets known. Both are associated with double star systems. Their sizes are unknown but are thought to be anything up to ten times the diameter of the sun. It is considered unlikely that they reflect enough light to make them visible at the distance of the earth—at least with present-day telescopes.

These objects bear little resemblance to the planets with which we are familiar. They may consist of small dark stars of a type about which little is known at present. (One such star, only a millionth as bright as the sun, was reported in 1944.) However, their existence certainly makes it possible that planets may not be as rare as was once suggested. Nevertheless, it has been pointed out that the inhabitants of these quasi-planets, if such exist, must find life decidedly difficult! For their planets move in highly eccentric orbits and they have two suns with which to contend. It is clear that an even climate would not be possible under these circumstances, for temperatures must fluctuate rapidly between extremes of hot and cold. No doubt we shall be hearing more about these fascinating stellar bodies in years to come—but the science of astronomy necessarily advances slowly.

We must conclude that, as yet, the existence of the quasi-planets throws little or no light upon the question to which we so badly want an answer—do genuine planetary systems exist elsewhere in the universe?[1]

In recent years a number of new theories have been advanced. An attempt has been made to account for the planets in terms of a *super-nova,* the debris from the explosion of which condensed in space near an attendant star. Magnetic forces have been invoked to enable the sun to collect interstellar matter in its journey through space and to turn it into planets. And so on. None of these views has gained much favour. But a theory developed, though in slightly different forms, by Otto Schmidt, Kuiper, Urey and others found widespread acceptance in the 1950–60 decade.

According to this view the planets were formed, in the first place, as cold bodies through the condensation of a cosmic cloud of dust and gas. According to the Russian school (Schmidt) the sun encountered the cloud on its travels through space.

The particles in the cosmic cloud jostled together and liberated energy which was radiated into space. In time a large number of bodies, ranging up to a hundred miles or so in diameter, were formed. These again collided with one another (the present asteroids are supposed to be the remnant of those which failed to do so) and for the most part were broken up. A few, however, failed to collide and these were then in a favourable position to collect the fragments from the others—and so they grew, quite slowly, into the original planets—or *proto-planets.* These were relatively large in size but heated up and lost matter, thus leaving the planets we know today.

This crude picture, too, bristles with difficulties and has been modified repeatedly with a view to obviating their force. One

---

[1] A summary of the evidence for the existence of such planets is given by M. H. Briggs (*Jour. Brit. Interplan. Soc.*, 1959, **17**, 59.) It seems very slender. Russian writers assert that even slight rhythmic changes in the light intensity of stars affords conclusive evidence of gyrating planets. But if space is *really* populated with intelligent beings (there are a million million planets in our galaxy alone, says Briggs), it is decidedly odd that evidence for flying saucers is so meagre. Why are there no crashed saucers in any of the world's museums? Surely a few space men must have perished in their astral adventure during geological time—and left some relics . . .? Of course the subject is most embarrassing. If we say that flying saucers do *not* exist, then it seems likely that intelligent beings are very rare in the universe: if we decide that they are genuine and that they have visited our globe at least occasionally over the past thousand million years, then it is sheer nonsense to pretend that science "proves" that all the life on earth has "evolved" from early forms—for many new species must often have been introduced from other worlds. We cannot have it both ways.

difficulty is that the chemical composition of the planets differs widely. This is overcome in the following way. A *super-nova* exploded and formed a ball of gas, much of which condensed into dust. At the centre the sun condensed—still at first quite cold—and farther out there were large masses—the proto-planets. As the super-nova explosion would give little or no hydrogen (hydrogen having been used up in stars which explode in this way) it is supposed that the dust cloud was composite—a mixture of a previous cloud of hydrogen and the new cloud formed by the explosion.

Soon atomic reactions started in the sun and it became hot, while the dust slowly cleared. The sun therefore shone on the proto-planets : they, too, became hot and much of their matter evaporated into space. Gradually they took up positions farther away from the sun. Then they began to grow once more. But as dust particles, (including ice and solid ammonia) began to rain upon them, they became very hot at the surface, hot enough to melt the surface rocks. In this way the planets were ultimately formed.

At the time of writing it seems doubtful if such views will fare better than their predecessors. Jeffreys objects that there are great difficulties in understanding how dust particles could unite in the way supposed—they would collide, be vaporized by the heat liberated through the collisions, and the gas would condense to form dust once more. If the theory is true, the matter which was evaporated from the proto-planets ought still to be in the solar system, but there is no sign of it. The difficulty occasioned by the large angular momentum of the planets is the same as with the collision theory, but this is no longer serious. In any case, Jeffreys believes it to be certain that, at some stage, the entire earth must have been liquid : "I do not see how the strong concentration of radioactive elements near the surface could have occurred except as a result of general fusion and recrystallization; and I know of no satisfactory alternative to the subsequent thermal contraction as an explanation for mountain building."[1] The earth would have cooled fairly rapidly, but as it must have been enveloped by a mantle of steam, this would have prevented loss of heat and prolonged the process enough to allow for the concentration of radio

[1] H. Jeffreys, *Nature*, 1952, **169**, 260, and *The Earth*, C.U.P., 1959. It may be noted that if the concentration of radioactive materials found in the rocks extended to great depths, the heat generated would result in the earth steadily becoming hotter. In any case—it could never have solidified.

elements near the surface. In confirmation of this view it has been found that the younger rocks contain more radium than the older.

In Russia the newer theories are strongly entrenched. It is said that they confirm the view that quite a large proportion of the stars have planets, so that the earth is no longer unique. This, of course, is comforting to those whose beliefs are materialistic. Lovell complains of this development in his Reith Lectures.[1] For two thousand years, he says, astronomical theory and religious doctrine were artificially kept in line. No doubt astronomy was hindered by lack of freedom. But now Communists reverse the situation—and he quotes Russian astronomers, such as Schmidt, in support. "Cosmogony in the U.S.S.R. is based on the firm materialist traditions of Russian science," "The rarity of planetary formations in Jeans's scheme opened the gates to idealism in cosmogony," "The development of cosmogony in the capitalist countries is hampered by the idealistic world outlook that prevails there." The same theme is propounded in popular Russian broadcasts which assure the masses that the last vestiges of theology in science have disappeared. Thus, according to Moscow radio, "Jeans's pseudo-scientific explanation of the origin of the earth approximated to the myth of creation. Soviet science has now completely exploded Jeans's theory."[2] And so on.

However, the same prejudices seem to be operating in the minds of many Western astronomers. Kuiper remarks, "The great frequency of planetary systems *appears comforting* to this writer when contemplating our solar system—which apparently is no freak of nature any more than the sun itself."[3] Urey writes in similar vein.

What is the upshot of this discussion? Firstly, that in theorizing upon events which took place long before man was on the scene, events which will never be repeated, it is unlikely that certainty will ever be reached. Secondly, that, even if general agreement is reached, it should not perhaps be taken too seriously. Russia is

[1] A. C. B. Lovell, *Listener*, November 20, 1958. Professor Lovell points out that, despite a large quota of astronomers in the U.S.S.R., there is no Russian school of astronomers concerned with the cosmological problem of the expansion and origin of the universe and that the translation of books dealing with the subject into Russian is banned. A remarkable admission on the part of the Russians that the origin of the universe cannot as yet be discussed in materialistic terms!

[2] *Listener*, December 20, 1951.

[3] G. P. Kuiper. *Jour. Roy. Ast. Soc. Canada*, 1956, **50** (several papers—the quotation is from the last *m. i.*).

pouring talent and money into astronomy on a scale which dwarfs the resources of much of the Western world. Since they make it difficult or impossible for any but materialists to study science at Universities and since the object of astronomical research in Russia appears to be to discount religion, we need hardly expect unprejudiced opinion in years to come. Thirdly, and lastly, even if the newer views are correct, it does not at all follow that our solar system is not still quite as rare and remarkable as seemed likely in the days of Jeans and Eddington.

For there are many questions still to be asked. What of the dust cloud? Where did it come from? The mixing of two kinds of cloud in space, a theory we have already alluded to, may be a rare event. And super-novae themselves are very rare—the commoner novae do not give temperatures high enough to form the heavier elements. And so on.

Thirty years back all seemed to be settled. Now all is speculation once more.[1]

MOON AND OCEAN

In the early days of the solar system the planets gyrated about the sun in orbits more elliptical than at present. Gradually they interacted with one another and their orbits became nearly circular. Possibly some collisions occurred. Probably enough there was a planet between Venus and Jupiter which, on breaking, formed the asteroids and meteorites. Moons may possibly have been formed from tides of molten rock pulled out by gravitational attractions. But in view of the doubts concerning the origin of the solar system, such matters cannot be settled.

As regards our own moon, too, there is, unfortunately, no approach to agreement among astronomers as to how it might have been produced. According to an old theory, popular in the earlier part of the present century, it chanced that at a particular period in

[1] The encounter theory may be due for another innings (Woolfson, *Nature*, 1960, **87**, 47). A near miss by a second star may have caused tides on the sun. Each time matter left the sun a gravity wave was set up so that matter was again lost after the lapse of a definite interval. There are still difficulties, to be sure, yet the main features of the solar system are *still* suggestive of an encounter theory. And from Russia there comes news (1960) that the centre of the earth is apparently much hotter than had hitherto been supposed, and in any case much hotter than can be accounted for, if the earth had been formed as a result of accretions of cold matter.

the earth's history the sun produced tides of molten rock that syn-
chronized with the natural period of oscillation of the earth. As a
result, a gigantic "resonance" tide was produced and much of the
matter of the earth left its parent body for ever, thus producing the
moon. Today, however, it is no longer considered possible that a
"resonance" tide could have been formed at any period in the
earth's history.

The circumstantial evidence does, however, still support the view
that the moon came from the earth. This is strongly suggested by
the fact that over practically the whole area of the Pacific Ocean,
the outermost granitic layer which chiefly covers the rest of the
earth, is missing. With the exception of small pieces carried there
by icebergs, granite is found neither on the bed of the Pacific nor
on any of its volcanic islands.[1] This suggests that the moon was
dragged out of the earth when the surface of the latter was in a
semi-plastic state. After this had happened, it would be easy for
the semi-molten magna below the already solidified granite, to
stream in from below and partly to fill the gigantic hole, leaving in
the end a depression which was later filled by water. At the same
time, the granite in the other parts of the earth might have broken
up into large pieces—thus producing smaller ocean basins. In this
way also it is possible to understand why it is that the earth is,
roughly speaking, covered with ocean on one side—an ocean surrounded by geological fault lines—while, in the main, the land
rises up out of the sea in the opposite hemisphere.

The same theory also accounts, readily enough, for the fact that
the moon possesses a much lower density than does the earth—the
central zone of metals being absent. This is just what we should
expect if the moon left the earth after the heavier materials had
separated out and become concentrated into the central regions of
the earth.

No satisfactory way of explaining how the moon could have left
the earth has been suggested. The combined angular momentum
of the earth and moon together are not enough to make the original
earth unstable. Perhaps a near encounter with another planet may
have caused the event, but mathematical difficulties and objections
are formidable. Perhaps they may yet be overcome.

[1] The only exception is that of Easter Island on the Albatross plateau, where
there are three dikes of obsidian—a granitic rock. The Albatross plateau, however,
is believed to have broken away from the mainland.

The moon, however, is no ordinary satellite so that it is likely that its origin may have been unusual too. The earth is the second smallest planet to possess a satellite, yet it possesses one of the heaviest satellites in the entire solar system. Four others are heavier but only slightly so.

Considered relatively to the size of the earth, the moon is by far the largest satellite in the solar system. It is $\frac{1}{82}$ of the mass of the earth, whereas Titan, which comes next, is only $\frac{1}{4,700}$ of Saturn.[1]

Something may now be said about the origin of the oceans. Here two views are possible. The water in the oceans may have formed a part of the surface of the earth, whether as vapour or liquid, from the very beginning. Alternatively, it may have been formed slowly over geological times. There is much evidence to indicate that the second of these views is correct. If we may assume that the earth was at one time molten (even if it had been cold at a yet earlier stage), laboratory investigations of rocks under pressure show that it must have solidified from below upwards. At the centre there settled a molten core of iron which did not solidify and is still liquid today. Above that came layers of rocks. Steam, nitrogen and acid vapours (hydrochloric acid, hydrofluoric acid and sulphur dioxide, in particular) were dissolved under pressure in the fluid melt. As the rocks at great depths solidified, some of the gases they contained bubbled up to the surface. At first there may have been much loss into space—at least, if the surface of the earth was hot. But soon this would no longer have happened, for the effective surface would have been a cool layer of cloud.

It is believed that the whole of the water in the sea arose in this way. When the oceans were first formed, however, they contained less water than they do today—estimates vary from about a third to a tenth. The rest of the water arose by volcanic action over a long period of geological time. How long we do not know. It was supposed until recently that pristine water was still entering the hydrosphere by volcanic action—for volcanoes emit large quantities of steam. But this is not so. Most of the steam from volcanoes is derived, ultimately, from sea water.

The early water contained much carbon dioxide and this leached the rocks, eventually forming the carbonates (chalk, dolomite, etc.)

[1] The satellite of Neptune, for which accurate measurements are not yet available, appears to be relatively larger than Titan, though smaller than the moon.

which we find in huge quantities today. More strongly acid vapours also helped to leach metals from the rocks.

Calculations by Goldschmidt show that the quantities of poisonous metals extracted from the rocks and so dissolved in the sea in early ages were so large that at that time it would almost certainly have been impossible for life to exist in the sea at all. But in nature a method of removing these harmful substances was employed which is identical in principle to that used today by the manufacturing chemist in the purification of his products, ordinary sugar, for example. In this, a very fine powder, usually charcoal, the particles of which have a large surface area, is added. Now vast quantities of iron were at one time dissolved in the sea and this iron was later precipitated as hydroxide and silicate, thus producing the sedimentary iron ores. Analysis shows that this fine precipitate removed practically all the poisonous elements in the sea.

We have already noted the value of the salt in the sea. But it is a remarkable fact that the sodium and the chlorine in salt (sodium chloride) must have had different origins, despite the fact that their quantities so nearly balance. The quantity of sodium in igneous rocks is fifty times greater than the chlorine required to combine with it. The chlorine, then, must have been provided by volcanic action and as the sodium would have been leached by the rocks at a fairly steady rate, mainly by rivers, it follows that throughout geological time the chlorine and the sodium must have kept in step with one another. If this had not happened, the ocean would have contained an excess of alkali or of acid and "a pronounced excess of either would have destroyed all life in the sea". But "There is no reason in the apparent origins of the sodium and the chlorine why an excess of any amount in either direction might not have accumulated, and the possibility of life becomes an accident."[1]

By now it is becoming evident that the story of the making of

[1] Sir H. Jeffreys, *The Earth, its Origin, History and Physical Constitution*, C.U.P., 1959, p. 265. To some extent as Jeffreys points out, the presence of calcium and magnesium compounds in addition to sodium helps to buffer the sea. But these metals are much less plentiful than sodium, and could only postpone the difficulty. It might be thought that the process would be self-regulating for, when more hydrochloric acid arose from volcanoes, the rate of leaching would increase, etc. But probably this is not so. If acid collected in the sea it would not evaporate and so would not be present in rain. Erosion rates by rivers would, then, be unchanged.

our planet is a remarkable one. A number of different circumstances seem to have combined together to make the earth a suitable
abode for life.

Whether or not, considered only from a physical point of view,
the formation of our solar system came about as a result of some
astronomically rare event we have no means of knowing. In view
of what we have learned, it is not unlikely. At all events we can be
certain that when we compare the earth with the other planets, all
the favours of fortune seem to have gone into its making. Situated
at the right distance from the sun, built to the right size, its radioactive elements concentrated in its crust, uniquely provided with a
satellite large enough to brighten the night and control the rhythm
of nature, rotating in such a way as to produce day and night and
seasonal variations in temperature, largely covered with water
which keeps the temperature more constant still, provided with
continents and ocean basins and with just about the right amount of
water to fill them, provided with an atmosphere of the right kind,
and with an ocean containing salt which enables clouds and rain to
form in the atmosphere but an ocean which, to preserve life over
geological time, has never developed strong alkalinity or acidity
and in which toxic metals have been removed by absorption on a
suitable precipitate—what more can we ask? Such are the facts.
The temptation to describe them teleologically has sometimes
proved irresistible—as difficult as it might be to say that an animal
has legs or eyes without saying also, or implying, that their purpose
is for walking or seeing. But is it possible that, on each occasion,
we should have invoked instead the long arm of coincidence?

At this point, perhaps, we have not yet learned enough to answer
this question for certain. But a very striking fact will have forced
itself on the reader's attention. It is this. With the exception of
recent speculations on the origin of the solar system which are in a
fluid state, the whole trend of recent research has been in the direction of making the earth appear a stranger and stranger place. We
met a similar situation in connexion with the creation. Since early
times, philosophers and scientists were quite content to imagine
that the universe was something which had always existed or were
disposed to imagine that it could have come into existence quite
"naturally". Discoveries in physics have now made that view appear
impossible or at least extremely unlikely. In the last chapters we
have seen that the trend of modern research in astronomy and

geophysics has been in the same direction. A century or so ago there appeared to be little that was particularly remarkable about the earth as the abode of living things. It was confidently supposed that all planets, stars and satellites could support life and the entire universe was supposed to be populated with beings. Today, while we certainly cannot prove that we are the only living creatures in the universe, we cannot but be impressed by the truly amazing conditions that must be satisfied in order that we may live.

M. M. Woolfson (see p. 86 f.n.) has developed his encounter theory with the aid of a computer (*Nature*, 1960, **188**, 1179). It is calculated that the tidal bulge on the sun oscillated with a period of seven years giving rise to a planet with each oscillation. Except for Mercury (difficult on *any* theory) the features of all the planets are well explained but the calculations indicate that two additional planets were formed between Mars and Jupiter. These may later have collided to form the asteroids.

Regarding the origin of the Pacific Ocean (see p. 87) E. R. Harrison has developed the theory that this was formed, not by the loss of the moon, but by the impact of a very large meteorite or asteroid, about 100 Km. in diameter. The exceptional character of this feature of the earth's topography is unaltered. (*Nature,* 1960, **188**, 1064).

CHAPTER VIII

CHEMISTRY OF LIFE

ORGANIZED matter can neither exist at very high temperatures, nor be built up from simpler materials at very low ones. Temperature alone, therefore, determines the rather narrow limits beyond which, above or below, life cannot adapt itself.

We have reached this conclusion as a result of a discussion in rather general terms, without reference to the particular *kind* of matter out of which we may imagine living organisms to be constructed. It is now time to consider the problem from this new angle.

Our first problem is this: Might living organisms have been built up out of any, or at least a considerable number, of the chemical elements, or are there reasons for believing that life itself imposes restrictions on the kind of matter which could have been used in this way?

ATOMIC JOINERY

In the early days of chemical science it was discovered that carbon possesses unique powers of combining both with itself and with other elements—especially nitrogen, hydrogen, and oxygen. But this by itself did not at once convince chemists that life was inconceivable without carbon. Even the most casual glance at the world of nature showed that carbon was not necessary for the existence of organized matter. Cloud formations, frost patterns, icicles, crystal growths in minerals, hard metals out of which complex machinery can be made—these and numerous other instances one and all proved that carbon was in no way necessary for the existence of organization. If the atoms in common salt can combine together to produce lumps of this material, there seemed no reason why a vital force should not also produce definite structures—wings, legs and eyes—out of salt.

Progress in science has undermined these plausible speculations. Early chemists possessed only the vaguest ideas as to how atoms become attached to one another. In recent times, however, four[1] different ways in which this may take place have been distinguished. Firstly there are certain very weak physical forces (known to chemists as *Van der Walls' force*—after their discoverer) which

FIG. 4.

The arrangement of sodium and chlorine atoms in a crystal of sodium chloride (common salt). The larger spheres represent the chlorine atoms and the smaller the sodium atoms, the sizes being represented approximately to scale. (After W. Barlow.)

(*Courtesy English Universities Press*)

only become important at low temperature. And they also sometimes enable very *large* molecules (such as the thread-like molecules of silk) to stick together. But they are too weak for normal adhesion of atoms and need be considered no further. Secondly,

---

[1] There are also the so-called *long range forces*, the nature of which is still not understood. They are important in biology but, being very weak, they could not function as a substitute for the bonds that join atoms together.

two atoms which have become electrically charged in opposite senses, attract one another strongly owing to the resulting electrical attraction. It is in this way that crystals of salts, including common salt, are held together. Yet it is a curious fact that, although electrical attractions are exceedingly strong, crystals (with the exception of the excessively thin so-called "whisker" crystals) are found to be very weak indeed.

The weakness has been tracked down to the fact that crystals are rarely ever perfect wholes. They contain what are known as "dislocations", or zones in which the parts of the pattern in a crystal do not quite achieve perfect interlocking. These dislocations can shift rapidly from place to place, giving rise to points of weakness.

If, then, living organisms were constructed of atoms held together by electrical attraction, they would crack and break in pieces. Perhaps this would be less likely to happen if they were of exceedingly small size—as might arise, for instance, if flies were about a million times smaller than they are. But even this is a wild flight of fancy, for there is another, fundamental, reason why organisms could not be built up in this way. The attraction between charged atoms is completely devoid of any *directive* quality: the atoms are only concerned to maintain the same *distance* between one another and, apart from this, they care nothing for organization.

To make this point clear we may imagine a kind of Alice-in-Wonderland teapot, on the atomic scale. We will consider the teapot to be a "compound" of pot, spout, lid and handle. But when we put the lid, spout and handle on the pot we find, to our consternation, that they do not stay where we put them, but proceed to slip round and round the pot, beneath it and above! If we lift the pot by the handle, the handle slides to the top and we cannot pour the tea. In short, considered as an *organized* structure, the teapot fails to fulfil a useful function—its parts might just as well have been joined together by string!

Fantastic as it sounds, the analogy gives us a passable picture of how atoms held together by electric charges behave. But the theme need not be pursued. No one now supposes that crystalline, salt-like animals are capable of existence. How little this point was appreciated in the past may be seen from the fact that in 1839, M. Gaudin sent to the *Academy of Sciences,* in Paris, details of a process by which, so he claimed, rock salt could be drawn out into ductile threads! The material "could be wound on a bobbin or converted into a solid tissue at will". The Academy is said to have been very impressed with the memoir: M. Arago thought the material would be ideal for torsion heads and for suspending the bobs of pendulums, while its investigation was sure to lead to great advances in theoretic physics.[1]

METALLIC ANIMALS

Thirdly, there is the *metallic bond*—the union between atoms that we find in the metals. Here the atoms, or at least some of them, lose electrons and become positively charged. The electrons remain in the metal in the form of a "gas" (it is the flow of this "gas" which constitutes the electric current) and the attraction between this "gas" and the positively charged atoms causes the whole mass to contract—so making metals dense. (Like most popular presentations of mathematical discoveries this picture is, of course, over-simplified, but it is accurate enough for our present purpose.)

But, again, metallic animals are a bizarre flight of fancy. Metals, like salts, are also held together by electric charges. In them, too, there is a lack of fixity of direction in the components of their architecture. And to this we must add difficulties connected with growth, reproduction and assimilation of food in imaginary metallic animals. And again, in no metal or metal alloy do we find anything approaching the gigantic strength of fibres of cellulose combined at the same time with the almost total lack of rigidity which enables us to bend these fibres in an effortless manner. Yet this combination of properties is essential for even the very simplest form of locomotion.

ATOMIC LINKS IN LIVING MATTER

Fourthly and lastly, there is true chemical union—known as *covalency* to chemists. In this atoms definitely combine with one another, instead of being held in place by forces operating at a distance. And, remarkably enough, the forces that are called into play, turn out to be *directive.* To revert to our wonderland-teapot analogy, we have at last found a way of attaching the lid, spout

[1] See *Athenæum*, May 18, 1839.

and handle in their proper places! No longer do they slide around: they stay where they are put.

The trick is done by electricity, to be sure. Electrons leave the atoms and join up in pairs, and each pair holds on tenaciously to two atoms, one on either side. Electrons seem to consist of little balls of electricity (perhaps they are vastly complicated inside—for the wonders and complexities of nature seem never-ending) which spin about an axis in the direction in which they are moving. But they can spin in a corkscrew sense or in an anti-corkscrew sense. And for some reason, perhaps connected with the magnetic fields that are set up, electrons of the two kinds keep together.

We find such chemical bonds in many familiar materials and always they are associated with enormous strength. Often, of course, the existence of this strength is not at once apparent. We have no means of catching hold of the ends of a molecule of oxygen, which contains two atoms, and pulling it apart. Yet, were we able to perform the experiment, we should be surprised at the resistance offered. When, however, molecules grow to a great size the strength reveals itself at once. For it often happens that when we try to pull a fragment of the material to pieces, we are actually pulling at the *molecules* and so are exerting our strength against the fundamental atomic forces of nature. The enormous strength of cellulose, silk and synthetic fibres is due to this circumstance. Weight for weight, cellulose is much stronger than steel yet, unlike steel, there is no resistance to bending. It is this fourth kind of atomic union— union by means of electron pairs—which holds the parts of animals and plants together.

Electron-pair bonds are readily made by about half the elements. But the different elements are extraordinarily particular about the way they let electrons behave themselves. The simpler atoms, from hydrogen to fluorine will not, even momentarily, permit more than eight electrons to come near them. Carbon behaves like this, but the heavier element, silicon, permits the approach of ten or even twelve electrons. Rapid chemical change depends upon the approach of these extra electrons with the result that carbon compounds are unchanged in air or water, whereas the corresponding silicon compounds react violently. And so, strangely enough, coal and wood do not inflame in air: human beings do not catch fire.

A few atoms, notably those of carbon and nitrogen, permit double or even triple electron-pair bonds to form: others, for example silicon, forbid any such nonsense! As a result, carbon dioxide, CO_2, or $O=C=O$ is a gas, but silicon dioxide, or quartz, SiO_2 is a solid containing only single bonds. Occasionally electron pairs join atoms of the same kind, thus arranging them in chains or strings. This, however, is rarely possible because, when once a chain begins to form, it gets progressively more fragile. But the carbon atom is a specialist at this chain-building game. Tens, hundreds, thousands—it matters not—of carbon atoms can join together and yet produce stable structures. No other element can compete.

Atoms are most choosy, too, about their mates. They attract some potential partners far more avidly than others. Chemists measure this "choosiness" by determining *bond energies.* The silicon atom, for instance, greatly prefers to be linked to oxygen, rather than to hydrogen, chlorine, or yet another silicon. But again carbon is remarkable: it is the friend of all. Its bond energies with hydrogen, chlorine, nitrogen, oxygen or even another carbon differ little. No other atom is like it. And this property is essential for life; without it the myriad reactions upon which life is based— reactions involving the reversible and energy-conserving replacements of atoms and groups of atoms involved in digestion, growth, reproduction, movement, etc.—would be impossible.

Carbon, in fact, is unique. The element most nearly resembling it is silicon. Until a few decades ago it was supposed that silicon, too, might form the backbone of complex molecules and become the basis of life—perhaps in distant worlds. But "we know enough now to be sure that the idea of a world in which silicon should take the place of carbon as the basis of life is impossible."[1]

The same or similar considerations apply to every other known element and, since all the stable elements have now been discovered or made in atomic piles, it may safely be said that they apply to *every* element. Carbon is the only element which can form compounds out of which organized living matter could conceivably be constructed. And the argument applies not only to our own earth but also to the distant stars. For there, also, the spectroscope reveals the same elements as those with which we are familiar on earth.[2]

[1] N. V. Sidgwick, *The Chemical Elements and their Components,* 1950, Vol I, p. 490.

[2] This point is still not recognized in some quarters. For example David Lack, in his otherwise excellent book, *Evolutionary Theory and Christian Belief,* 1957, p. 64, critizes the teleological argument of Lawrence Henderson and C. F. A. Pantin and

PHANTASY—DEMIURGE AT WORK

Let us now, just for the fun of it, imagine ourselves once again in the position of Plato's *demiurge*—the senior angel to whom, according to the Greek philosophers, the Almighty gave the rather undignified task of creating the world.

We are now about to make living matter. Where shall we start? Around us we find a hundred kinds of atoms—half of them common and the rest rare. We examine them in turn. We experiment with likely ones in our starry laboratory. Soon we find that carbon is the most promising with which to make a start. All the others seem useless or only suitable to be fastened to a carbon framework.

As we continue our researches we find, with increasing astonishment, that it is not a case of "carbon will do", but that the carbon atoms have all the properties we could desire. It is as if the Creator has given us a kit of prefabricated parts ready made for the work in hand.

We have decided to use carbon. But now a serious difficulty arises. How shall we arrange that a supply of carbon shall always be at hand? It would serve little purpose to create plants and animals and then leave them to their fate, with the sure knowledge that when once they and their progeny had used up all the carbon in some local deposit of this material, they would rapidly become extinct. Again, what would happen to them if for some reason migration became necessary? Should we be satisfied if life were confined to a few spots here and there, where mineral deposits of carbon happened to lie near the surface?

It might be possible so to construct the earth that all rocks would contain some carbon. But even then it would be quite difficult for living creatures to obtain adequate supplies—what if the surface layers became exhausted? Another plan would be to dissolve a carbon-containing compound in the sea—but that might only serve to limit life to water.

---

remarks: "This argument is very weak. It assumes that there can be no life except in the forms in which we know it, and there seems to be no intrinsic reason [*sic*] why life of some sort should not exist in a world of very different physical and chemical make-up than our own." But Lack omits all discussion of chemistry in his book, and seems quite unaware of the strength of the argument he dismisses as "very weak".

The most reasonable plan would be to place the carbon in the air—since air is the only material disseminated over the whole earth. For this, a gaseous compound of carbon would be necessary. But such a compound would also have to fulfil certain rather exacting conditions.

First of all, the compound would have to be highly oxidized for, if it were not, and if the air contained the reactive element oxygen, lightning flashes, forest fires and other natural events would soon destroy it completely. It would seem, then, that the compound would have to be an oxide—the oxide of carbon containing the maximum possible amount of oxygen.

This oxide must not be very soluble in water, or other suitable liquid, as otherwise rain would "wash" it out of the air. On the other hand, a good deal must dissolve in water, for chemical changes are slow unless reacting substances are in the dissolved state. Underwater life would also require a supply of carbon.

This means that, on shaking our carbon-containing gas with water, it should divide itself more or less equally between the aqueous and the gaseous phases. Carbon dioxide might be the compound we require. If this will not do, it seems that nothing can take its place. It is the oxide of carbon richest in oxygen, and so it will be stable in an oxygen-containing atmosphere. But are its properties what we desire?

We find, with delight, that the gas dissolves in about an equal volume of water, so that it will not be removed from air by rain but will always be available in water and atmosphere alike. But oxides are troublesome compounds. In water they usually give powerful acids or bases. This would not do at all. What we need is a very weak acid, one just about as strong as water (for water may be considered as an acid), one that will not interfere with the valuable properties of water for which it would be hard to find an alternative (see later, p. 102). The strengths of acids vary by factors of billions. We consult tables of these strengths—hardly two are close together and none close to that of water. Anxiously we measure the strength of the acid that is formed when our gas dissolves in water.

The incredible happens again! It comes right! [1]

[1] The value of pK_1 for carbonic acid is about 6·5 (for water, about 6·9). Since the carbonic acid concentration in water is proportional to the concentration of carbon dioxide in the gas with which the water is in equilibrium, it follows that carbon dioxide buffers water near neutrality.

It appears, then, that chemistry limits our choice to carbon dioxide. This is one of the factors, not hitherto discussed in detail, which imposes rather stringent astronomical conditions upon the size of our planet. If we make the planet large like Jupiter or Saturn, carbon will exist only in the form of methane, the properties of which make it unsuitable as a source of carbon for living matter. If, on the other hand, we make it as small as Mercury or the moon we shall have no carbon dioxide or atmosphere present at all.

SOURCE OF ENERGY

Let us suppose that all these preliminary matters have been arranged in a satisfactory manner. We now direct our attention to the building of giant carbon-containing molecules out of the carbon dioxide which we have agreed to make available in atmosphere and sea.

At once a difficulty of some magnitude arises. When carbon burns to produce carbon dioxide it liberates a great deal of heat— with one exception, more than that liberated by any other solid element. This means that the energy of carbon in carbon dioxide is, so to speak, at a very low level and, if we are to produce other carbon compounds from it, we shall have to provide for an abundant energy supply. Where is this energy to come from?

We survey the various forms of energy that might be available on the surface of a planet. Chemical energy would seem to offer possibilities but it would very rapidly become exhausted unless it could be continually replenished. Tidal energy and the energy of the wind are other possible sources, but as such energy is in a wholly unsuitable form, a very elaborate mechanism would be necessary to transform it—and suitable machinery could hardly be made available to life all over the globe. The same objection applies to most other sources of terrestrial energy.

Radioactive substances might, at first sight, afford a way out of the difficulty, provided these were present in sufficiently large amount. But unfortunately the energy they liberate is very destructive; it would scarcely be possible for delicate cells to function satisfactorily if they were always subjected to bombardment by high-speed atomic particles!

PLANTS AND ANIMALS

The only remaining source of energy, or at least of energy in a sufficiently concentrated form, would be that derivable from an adjacent star. To obtain the largest possible amount of energy from this star, living organisms would need, as far as possible, to be flat —exposing a large area to the light and air. This consideration might lead us to the idea of leaves.

If, in addition to vegetable life, we wish for creatures that can move about from place to place, it is clear that they will have to function according to a different plan. Animals would be most inefficient if they resembled walking trees with vast root systems which they would be obliged to bury or dip in streams from time to time. It would be more feasible for such creatures to rely on plants for their supply of ready prepared carbon compounds. The latter could then be "burnt" up by the animals, which would return carbon dioxide into the air. By this means, the way would be open for both plants and animals to use and re-use the same atoms of carbon over and over again, while the animals would be provided with the necessary energy to live their lives.

All this is, of course, just what we find in nature, and it seems to be the only convenient arrangement possible. Thus the general features of plant and animal life look as if they have been planned exactly as we ourselves should probably have planned them had we known nothing of the arrangements that actually exist.

WHY WATER?

Another point of great importance in connexion with living matter is concerned with the function of water in nature.

Chemical reactions which take place in the solid state are immeasurably slow and we have already had occasion to observe that if carbon dioxide is to be used as a source of carbon in the building up of carbon compounds, the process must be allowed to take place in presence of a liquid.

Any liquid will not serve the purpose. The liquid must be one which can easily be made available from elements which are common in the universe or at least on the surface of a planet. It must also be a good solvent and one in which reactions readily occur.

Only very few liquids fulfil these conditions, even partially. Formamide, liquid hydrocyanic acid, and molten urea are excellent solvents but are far too unstable for use on a planet. Moreover, they could not exist permanently side by side with free oxygen in the atmosphere. The same observation applies to ammonia, which, although in some ways suitable, would either have to be kept at too low a temperature for life, or else at a pressure high enough to keep it liquid—in which event an enormously thick atmosphere through which little light could penetrate would become necessary. Liquid hydrogen fluoride has been speculatively suggested. Like water it is a good solvent, even for proteins, but it is too reactive a material and possesses the great limitation that, unlike water and ammonia, but like hydrocyanic acid, it gives "bases" and neutral substances in solution, but not "acids".[1] The vapour, also, is very heavy—the importance of this point will appear in the sequel.

The more carefully the matter is considered, the plainer does it become that there is one liquid and only one, namely *water*, which fulfils the necessary conditions. Water, therefore, would have to be chosen. And, as we have seen in an earlier chapter, its high specific heat makes it ideally suited for maintaining the constancy of the planet's temperature.

Once again the cycle closes. Water, as we have noted, is the only cosmically abundant liquid which could be used for thermostating a planet. Now we find that it alone is suitable for the needs of life. We have started, in imagination, to investigate the possibility of living organisms. Again and again we have found, in astonishment, that what would otherwise be baffling difficulties, have been solved in advance. Creation itself contained the seeds of things to come.

---

[1] The use of these words calls for some explanation—but a knowledge of chemistry is required. Water and ammonia are self-ionizing solvents: $2H_2O \rightleftharpoons H_3O^+ + OH^-$; $2 NH_3 \rightleftharpoons NH_4^+ + NH_2^-$. Hydrochloric acid and ammonium chloride are "acids" in water and ammonia respectively, because they increase the H_3O^+ (i.e. H^+ and H_2O) and NH_4^+ (H^+ and NH_3) respectively. Similarly NaOH and NaNH$_2$ are alkalis because they increase the OH^- and NH^-_2. Hydrofluoric acid also ionizes: $2HF \rightleftharpoons H_2F^+ + F^-$. In this solvent KF is a "base" since it increases the F^-. But only very rarely is an acid formed—no instances were known until 1957.

The choice of water as the main liquid on our planet at once imposes temperature restrictions a great deal narrower than those that previously seemed necessary. For if water is to remain a liquid, and not turn into ice or steam (in neither of which would reactions take place), it must be maintained between its freezing-point and its boiling-point, or, say, between approximately $-10°$ and $130°$ C. And towards the upper part of this range, water becomes so corrosive and so reactive and its vapour pressure so high (thus cutting off the sun's rays) that life might well be impossible for any length of time.

Arising out of the presence of water, carbon dioxide and oxygen on the surface of our planet, it would also be necessary to replace the oxygen as it was used up by animals. This could best be done by plants, the oxygen coming directly or indirectly from carbon dioxide. To suggest a mechanism by means of which carbon dioxide could be made to give free oxygen in presence of sunlight, is still beyond the wit of man at the present stage of chemical science —for the mystery that lies behind photosynthesis has not been solved, despite much recent progress.

FURTHER SPECIFICATIONS

It will at once be apparent that, so far as the general economy of nature is concerned, arrangements seem to have been made similar to or identical with those that we should probably have planned ourselves. In other words, nature is beginning to show all the characteristics of a planned whole.

Yet clearly we have only touched the fringe of the question. The chemical ordering of nature must go far deeper than anything which has so far been mentioned in this chapter. For with the exception of a reference to photosynthesis, we have been concerned only with fundamental principles.

Let us imagine an analogy. A scientist in 1800 might have pointed out that in order to make a workable motor-car, it would be necessary to attach wheels to a body or chassis and that some chemical fuel, solid or liquid, would be required to provide energy. His statements would have been correct so far as they went, but engineers of a later period would insist that other things also were necessary—a differential gear to stop wear of tires on the driving wheels, a cooling system to remove unwanted heat and so on.

It is the same with life. If we knew precisely how a plant could be made to store the sun's energy, how an animal could turn chemical into mechanical energy, how complex proteins could be made to function as enzymes, and so on, we should certainly demand much more exacting conditions to be fulfilled before we started our experiment in world-building.

As to what these new conditions may be, we as yet know very little. But, as we shall see in the sequel, our knowledge of this subject is now beginning to accumulate slowly.[1]

[1] For useful discussions of the problems raised in this and the following chapter, see especially, N. V. Sedgwick, *Science*, 1937, **86**, 335; L. J. Henderson, *The Fitness of the Environment*, 1931 and *The Order of Nature*, 1917; E. J. Hartung, *Chemical Engineering and Mining Review*, 1934, **26**, 173; H. F. Blum, *Time's Arrow and Evolution*, 1951 and C. F. A. Pantin, Organic Design, *Advancement of Science*, 1951, **8**, 138.

CHAPTER IX

ELEMENTS

"It may not be wholly unreasonable to fancy that to almost every element there falls some unique and indispensable role in the economy of nature."

Sir Cyril Hinshelwood. Presidential Address to the
Chemical Society, 1948. (*Journal*, 1948, p. 531.)

OXYGEN

WE have seen that carbon possesses remarkable properties that make it suitable as a material out of which the framework of living organisms may be constructed. But in recent years it has become increasingly clear that other elements beside carbon have unique properties which makes them suitable for the building up of living matter. The properties of oxygen, though less readily appreciated and described, are probably as important as those of carbon. Oxygen enters into the composition of water and carbon dioxide and is partly, at least, responsible for the remarkable properties of these materials. It differs from sulphur and the other elements (those with six outer electrons) with which it is classed in chemistry in a number of important ways—it is, for example, the only gaseous element among them, while its power of combining with other elements and liberating an enormous amount of energy in the process is unparalleled with the exception of fluorine.

Exploration by means of rockets shows that the earth is bathed in very short-wave radiation (in the co-called Schumann region) of great intensity. Oxygen completely absorbs this radiation, which is fatal to life.

Under the influence of short-wave radiation oxygen forms ozone. At a great height in the atmosphere this gas forms in amount equivalent to a layer 0·3 cm. thick, measured at ordinary pressure. The importance of the ozone layer cannot be overstressed. It shuts off also the nearer ultraviolet light—as effectively, it is said, as if the whole earth were enveloped in half a dozen layers of gold leaf. It is one of the most opaque gases known, perhaps the most opaque. Were it not for the presence of the ozone layer, life would be virtually impossible on earth, for the sun's rays would rapidly kill all small living organisms. It is noteworthy that ozone only forms in the upper atmosphere where it can do no damage—it is a highly toxic gas, rapidly fatal to plant life.

Oxygen plays an important part in the physical structure of the earth, for the rocks consist of silicates (that is, they contain silicon combined with oxygen). How far it is indispensable in this connexion we do not yet know, but it may well be that an earth made of sulphides, silicides, borides or other compounds of metals would be too fragile to form a stable structure.

HYDROGEN

The properties of hydrogen are equally if not more remarkable, and some of them have only come to light in comparatively recent years. Cosmically hydrogen provides the source of energy of the stars, our sun included. In turning to helium a vast store of energy is given up. Carbon is the catalyst for the reaction and here carbon assumes an important role which could not, it appears, be delegated to any other common element.

It has long been known that hydrogen combines strongly with certain other elements, often liberating much heat, as when it is exploded with oxygen or chlorine. In this way an atom of hydrogen becomes attached to one and only one atom of another element. But after this has happened it still possesses the power of combining with a second atom in a manner which has aptly been likened to that of a zipp fastener. The resulting *hydrogen bond* (it is not a true chemical bond but an electrostatic attraction) has formed the subject matter of much recent research and its importance can hardly be exaggerated.

Chemical changes are normally associated with the liberation or absorption of a great deal of energy which manifests itself in a rise or fall of temperature. The energy associated with the hydrogen bond is, however, very small, with the result that, by means of hydrogen, it becomes possible for strong unions to be established between atoms without large concomitant energy changes.

The hydrogen bond is unique in chemistry, and without it life would be difficult and probably impossible. It is most unlikely, for instance, that any conceivable kind of efficient muscle could be made to function without hydrogen bonds.

Other biological mechanisms are also believed to depend upon the hydrogen bond. It appears likely that the protein molecules are able to wind, unwind and rewind themselves into new and stable structures, held together by hydrogen bonding. Following suggestions by Pauling it is widely believed that the body manufactures specific antibodies to invading organisms by such means. It is believed that hydrogen bonds are largely responsible for the union of "antigen" and "antibody", a union upon which natural immunity to disease depends. It is also considered possible that they are involved in the action of enzymes—chemical substances about to react in the body first of all fastening themselves on to large enzyme molecules by means of hydrogen bonds, and a special reaction then taking place because one of the molecules has been arranged in a particular way with the right groups exposed.

WATER

The hydrogen bond is also important in another way. Upon its existence some of the remarkable properties of water depend. It is due to hydrogen bonding that water is a liquid—H_2O would be a gas, difficult to condense, like H_2S. Hydrogen bonding also gives to water its wonderful solvent properties. But from the fact that water is not H_2O, but $(H_2O)_n$ (n = 2, 3 or more), one would be led to expect that water-vapour would be heavier than air. (The argument will be found in any elementary textbook of chemistry.) Even if the vapour were H_4O_2 at ordinary temperatures, the vapour would still be so dense that when the sun shone on the sea the evaporated water would simply lie as a thick vapour over the surface instead of rising upwards. We may well imagine what this would mean—high clouds would not form, nor would water pass from the sea to the dry continents. Moreover, the sea itself might rarely be free from thick mist.

A cosmic architect, faced with the problem of designing the elements, might well reach the conclusion that no possible properties of water were compatible with the uses for which it was required. Either the water must be simple H_2O, in which case it would not be a liquid at all but a light gas and possess no solvent properties, *or* it must be H_4O_2 or H_6O_3, etc., in which case it could never spread through the atmosphere of a planet.

How has the problem been solved in nature? The answer is that as water evaporates from the surface of the sea, the molecules at once break up to form H_2O and combine again when the water condenses. This behaviour is probably unparalleled throughout the whole realm of chemistry.[1]

Water possesses many other curious properties, most of which are apparently connected with the presence of hydrogen bonds. The liquid has a maximum density at $4°$ C., a fact that is of considerable value in nature for it means that if a water surface is cooled from above, the lower layers will not normally cool below $4°$ C. Then there is the fact that ice is less dense than water and floats on the surface of the latter—a behaviour that is found paralleled in only a very few other substances (metallic bismuth and boric anhydride). This behaviour is again of the greatest value in nature—not only does it help to save aquatic life in the winter time, but water by penetrating into the crevices of rocks, breaks them up when the water freezes and in this way soil is produced.

Other properties of water about which little is known may be of extreme value. Thus, were it not for the high reflectivity of ice and snow (93 per cent from freshly fallen snow as compared with 25 per cent from the surface of the sea), we may be certain that flooding after a heavy snowfall would always be severe. But in this and some other instances we do not yet possess sufficient data to be able to say whether the properties of water are unusual.

NITROGEN

Turning to the element nitrogen we see how, like carbon, its properties once again synchronize with the requirements of life. Like carbon it is available in the atmosphere: as with the carbon cycle, so there is a nitrogen cycle which ensures that the element will always be available on our planet.

As a constituent of the atmosphere, we deem nitrogen common: but cosmically it is rare. The properties of the element are most

---

[1] A near analogy to water is afforded by nitrogen dioxide, NO_2, the liquid form of which has the formula N_2O_4, but this does not turn into NO_2 on evaporation. The vapour always consists of a mixture of N_2O_4 and NO_2 the relative proportions of the two depending upon the temperature. Hydrofluoric acid behaves similarly.

abnormal. Like phosphorus and arsenic, the atom has five outer electrons but, unexpectedly, the element does not exist in the form of tetrahedrally-shaped molecules containing four atoms of nitrogen each (compare P_4, As_4). When phosphorus is burnt in air it liberates much energy: this energy falls regularly through As (arsenic), Sb (antimony) to Bi (bismuth). If chemists had not discovered nitrogen they would probably predict that it would be more reactive than phosphorus (just as, in neighbouring groups, oxygen is more reactive than sulphur, fluorine than chlorine and carbon than silicon). It might be a volatile liquid, exploding violently with oxygen. But no. It forms the N_2 molecule—astonishingly unreactive, stable even with oxygen. Its oxide gives nitric acid with water and this, as expected, is an acid: so this time it is the free element, not its oxide (as with carbon) which possesses the unexpected properties.

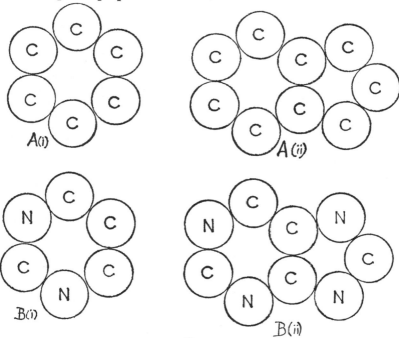

FIG. 5.

A(i) and A(ii) represent carbon (C) ring systems of great stability. In B(i) and B(ii) two and four, respectively, of the carbon atoms are shown replaced by nitrogen (N) atoms. The size of a nitrogen atom is almost the same (slightly smaller) as that of a carbon. These B-ring structures, which are widespread in nature, are astonishingly stable—far more so than the A kind.

Nitrogen is an essential constituent of the nucleic acids, out of which chromosomes are made, and also of the twenty amino-acids which form the proteins.

Chains of carbon atoms readily form rings, those with five or six atoms being particularly stable. The most familiar compound of this kind is benzene, C_6H_6, which contains a ring of six carbon atoms. Nitrogen has the unique property that it can replace carbon (CH) in these rings, the resulting structures becoming progressively (to a point) more stable. For example, the ring system arrangements shown at A (Fig. 5) are very stable, but those shown in B much more so. These are the two ring systems found in the nucleic acids, but they are found also in many other natural products. Here we find frameworks of extraordinarily enduring properties which can be handed on from one generation to the next with little chance of decomposition. The enormous mass of "information" necessary for the reproduction of animal or plant is stored in the nucleic acid molecules. These have been compared to a library of several thousand volumes—but the volumes themselves endure because of the properties of nitrogen.

Nitrogen is one of only three elements (nitrogen, oxygen and fluorine) which form hydrogen bonds. The formation of these bonds is, as we have noted, basically important in the chemistry of life. The ability of nitrogen to take a positive charge (as in ammonium salts) and lose it again easily (as when ammonium salts form ammonia) is remarkable. Though years of exploration lie ahead, it seems likely that this property—shown far more strongly by nitrogen than by any other element—is basic to biological reproduction. Nucleic acid molecules are connected to form chromosomes in the form of a double helix. (Compare the screws with multiple starts, in this case two, as used by the engineer.) In reproduction it is believed that the helix comes apart, beginning to form two single helixes. As they are being formed these pick up nucleic acid molecules from the surrounding fluid and so become double once more. (The process is not spontaneous but requires a catalyst —an enzyme—to effect it.) The coming apart of the two helixes must, in some way, be connected with the chemistry of nitrogen, for the helixes are held together by hydrogen-bonded nitrogen and oxygen. The spiral which exactly fits together and, by playing on variations in four N-ring compounds, enshrines the genetic code, is evidently a structure of wonderful beauty and ingenuity. Our

understanding of it (due to Watson and
Crick, 1954) has been described as "one
of the most beautiful scientific concepts
of our time" (Perutz).

Though our knowledge is fragmentary,
it is evident that nitrogen must have a
number of highly specific properties which
fit it for the end in view. Had one of
these properties failed to conform exactly
with requirements, nitrogen would have
been useless in biology and no other
element could have taken its place.

COMPARING ELEMENTS

It is true that the simplest elements
often differ markedly from those that follow them in the usual chemical classifica-
tion. Yet, in the elements we have been
considering, the differences are such as
almost to compel us to the view that they
were in some way planned for the needs
of life. This appearance becomes all the
more telling if we compare the properties
that we have noted with those of some of
the simple compounds that are not involved in ordinary biological reactions.

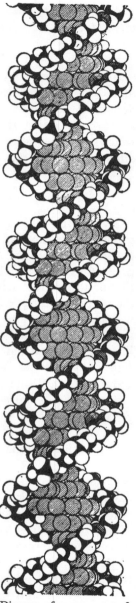

FIG. 6.

(By courtesy of
Dr. M. H. Wilkins)

PHOSPHORUS

CARBON IN
SUGAR-PHOSPHATE
BACKBONE

CARBON AND
NITROGEN
IN BASES

OXYGEN

HYDROGEN

Carbon monoxide, CO, for example,
which is not normally formed in nature, is
remarkable in many ways. But its pecu-
liarities seem in no way related to the
needs of life. If CO_2 had had properties
like those of CO, life would have been
either impossible or very limited.

Diagram of arrangement of
atoms in a nucleic acid (de-
soxyribonucleic acid, DNA)
molecule.

Again, we have seen that in combinations that are biologically important, nitrogen differs from other elements in a rather striking way. But this is not so in its compounds with metals—nitrides are very similar to phosphides and arsenides, etc. Here, therefore, nitrogen exhibits no very striking properties. This is just as we might expect if the elements were designed, for nitrides are of no importance to life and are never formed in living organisms. The same consideration applies also to carbon, for metallic carbides which are never formed in animals and plants do not appear to differ in any very striking way from silicides, borides, etc.

OTHER ELEMENTS

Five of the nine simplest elements have no obvious biological significance. Among these, also, but especially in boron and fluorine, we find elements with curious properties which find no parallels in chemistry. Yet boron and fluorine are both necessary for life, or at least for many forms of life, and are conspicuous among the so-called trace elements. Their function, however, is still unknown. It is at least possible that one day, when our knowledge is less superficial, we may find that they, too, fit into the general "design" of the world—that they, too, are just the kind of elements we should have had to create if we had been in the position of God about to create His universe.

It may be relevant here to note that the common form of calcium phosphate, *apatite,* contains two —OH groups. When fluorides come into contact with this material, the —OH is replaced by F. The resulting material has a quite remarkable hardness. Animals make use of it in the enamel of their teeth. Again, only fluorine behaves in this way; without it reasonably durable teeth might have been impossible. It would be extremely hard to find any other low-temperature reaction which would make a material of comparable hardness and durability. Fluorine may, of course, fulfil other biological roles as well.

Turning now to the heavier elements, it may be said at once that, with a few exceptions, very little is known about the way in which they fit into the general pattern of life. However, even here, our limited knowledge suggests that something akin to intelligence has been at work. For instance, it is obviously necessary that there should be an abundant supply of an element, some of the compounds of which should be soluble in water, so that it may be readily available, and others insoluble, so that hard parts such as bones may be built up. Calcium seems to fill this role exactly, though here, perhaps, it is not the only element which might do so.

Indications point to the view that sodium and potassium, dissolved in sap or blood, are necessary for higher forms of life, but we do not know precisely what function they fulfil. Again, several elements have the power of nearly fitting inside the flat system made by the joining together of four pyrrole nuclei that we find so abundantly distributed throughout nature (see Fig. 7). In blood, iron seems to be necessary, though copper or vanadium might do instead. In chlorophyll, the green material of plants which is essential for photosynthesis, the central atom is one of magnesium and nowhere in all nature do we find that this can be

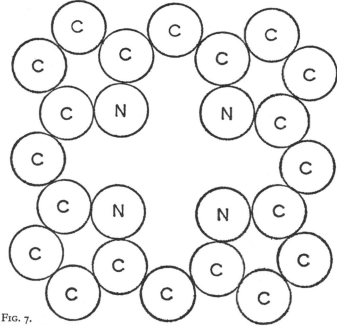

FIG. 7.

The figure shows a natural ring system containing four nitrogen (N) atoms. The structure is flat and astonishingly stable. A metal atom (not shown) is found at the centre (magnesium in chlorophyll, iron in the haemoglobin of blood, also copper, vanadium, etc.). The outermost carbon (C) atoms are found linked with various groups and structures which are not shown. In vitamin B_{12} an atom of cobalt lies at the centre but two of the four 5-membered pyrrole rings are joined *directly* together, instead of through a carbon atom.

replaced by any other element. It is evident that magnesium possesses a unique property which enables it to fulfil this role, but we do not yet know why it alone can do so. In the periodic chart of the elements we place it in Group 2, with beryllium, calcium, strontium and barium, coming between the first two, and with two electrons in its outer orbit. In most respects it seems normal, but not in its strong tendency to combine with nitrogen, the property made use of in plants.

The same arrangement of atoms is encountered in several of the enzymes and it appears that in a number of these a central atom of one particular element, and no other, enables the enzyme to function. As an example, the enzyme *carbonic anhydrase,* which enables the blood to dissolve and to give up carbon dioxide rapidly, contains zinc.

Other similar instances have been discovered. Cadmium has been found in an enzyme present in horse-liver. Selenium is an essential trace element in the rat and perhaps in other mammals too; it may be essential and is certainly very beneficial for plant growth. Vanadium (essential in green plants), molybdenum (necessary for nitrogen fixation in soil), manganese and copper are of great importance to life. Some plants and animals concentrate gold, germanium, lithium, strontium, etc., and apparently make good use of them. And so on.

Fifty years ago it was supposed that ten elements were needed for life—today the list is longer, perhaps twenty, and it is likely to become longer still. But in this field discovery is slow. It is very difficult to obtain materials sufficiently pure to detect the need for 1 part in 100,000,000 (the figure for molybdenum) of a trace element.

Facts such as these certainly suggest that a number of the elements which are required by living organisms in minute traces, possess properties that are each in their own way indispensable. This conclusion is strengthened by the fact that plants and animals pick out rare atoms from soil or diet and make use of them to perform various functions. It would seem reasonable to suppose that if the purposes for which they are used *could* be performed by making use of the commoner elements only, this would undoubtedly be done—especially as rare atoms are often virtually absent in many localities.

Thus as research progresses, there are increasing indications that, just as carbon possesses unique properties which fit it for the building up of organisms, so also, in a more subtle way, do a great many of the other elements.

IODINE, PHOSPHORUS, COBALT

In recent years, developments in the study of the elements iodine, phosphorus and cobalt have done much to substantiate this conclusion.

Biochemists have often expressed amazement at the way in which iodine enters into animal life. Taking the world at large iodine is an exceedingly rare element. Ordinary rocks contain about a third of a gram per ton while there is only a gram of the element in fifty-five tons of sea water. Moreover, iodine scarcely ever enters as an essential constituent into minerals. We owe its relative cheapness only to the fact that there are some large natural concentrations of the element—notably in the Chile nitrate beds.

Brown and red seaweeds, bath sponges and corals extract iodine from seawater and transform it into the substance *diiodotyrosine*. No one has shown that this material is of use to them—indeed, in the corals, it exists in the horny tissue on which the living cells sit and diiodotyrosine has all the appearances of being an excretory product. Apart from these rather unusual instances, iodine does not appear to be of any value to lower organisms. Yet this rare element is turned by mammals, first of all into the diiodotyrosine, then into the more complex substance *thyroxine,* which circulates around the body combined with a protein, and finally into *triiodothyronine* which regulates the rate of functioning of cells. A mechanism, little understood as yet, enables the thyroid glands to pick the minute traces of iodine out of the foodstuffs which enter the body and to build them up into the required substances.

As far as we know no other substance can replace thyroxine and it is employed, not only by all mammals but even by amphibia— tadpoles will not turn into frogs without it. Professor Mason has well remarked: "A teleologist might well find in this hormone molecule the sole *raison d'être* of the element iodine."[1]

Turning to the element phosphorus—it has long been known that this is one of the trace elements, necessary in small quantities in all forms of life. But only in recent years has the reason for this

[1] Irvine Mason, *Royal Institution Lecture,* December 3, 1937.

become apparent. The phosphoric acid radical possesses a remarkable property of joining up with itself to produce short chains,
and when these chains are broken, energy is liberated in fairly large
amounts. But the energy stored in this way is directly related to
the energy evolved when certain other reactions occur.[1] Were it
not for this fortuitous—if it be fortuitous—equality of the energies,
it is difficult to believe that life would be possible. Once again,
therefore, we are confronted by the fact that the properties of
phosphorus are apparently "designed" to meet a particular need. If
the properties of phosphorus were but slightly different, it seems
certain that no other element could have taken its place.

Let us turn to cobalt. For more than half a century, since the
days of Alfred Werner, chemists have wondered at the curious
properties of this element. Its atoms easily attract to themselves
other atoms or groups and fix them firmly in the positions of the
corners of an imaginary octohedron (Fig. 8).

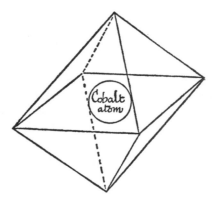

FIG. 8. COBALT ATOM.

The positions can be occupied by many variants, and multitudes
of stable, often beautifully coloured, compounds have been prepared, many of them by Werner. Why all this? A mere curiosity?
Or has cobalt, like carbon, a niche in nature which only it can fill?

It had long been known that the "coast disease" of sheep in
South Australia could be cured by iron. Until the 1920's an iron
ore, brought from a great distance, was used as a sheep lick. Then
a nearer mine was opened up and the new ore used instead.

[1] See later, p. 135.

Chemically, there seemed to be no difference, but the sheep at once ailed. Samples were sent to England where the spectroscope detected a minute trace of cobalt in the original ore. When cobalt was added to the sheep lick, the animals recovered.

Gradually it became apparent that mammals need cobalt. Eventually a beautifully crystalline, bright red, cobalt-containing substance, vitamin B_{12}, was isolated from bone. It has the property of enabling the bone marrow to manufacture red blood corpuscles: without it anaemia develops.

The brilliant work of Todd (Nobel Prize, 1958), Hodgkin and others has led to the complete elucidation of the structure of vitamin B_{12}. In the centre is the cobalt atom, arranged as in Werner's compounds. Around it are four pyrrole nuclei almost as in haemoglobin (Fig. 7). On one side is a cyanide group which easily allows of displacement. Various chains hold the molecule together, giving a structure of some complexity—though simple by biological standards.

Why is the cobalt necessary? How does vitamin B_{12} work? We do not yet know. But the generally held view is that the cobalt atom somehow brings powerful forces to work, arranging surrounding atoms to produce the framework—the four pyrrole nuclei and perhaps some of the side-chains—that are necessary for the making of blood. If this turns out to be so, it is only what a teleologist might have expected. Again use will have been made of a rare kind of atom. If that atom had not been there at the start, should we have been here to tell the tale?

THE TEACHING OF CHEMISTRY

Instances of this kind suggest that an entirely new approach to chemistry may one day be possible in education. At the present time the student of inorganic chemistry is confronted by a bewildering mass of facts that seem arbitrary and unrelated. But we are now beginning to see that the elements have a purpose, so that it should ultimately be possible to teach chemistry from a teleological point of view. The student would then be given the exciting task of imagining that he, together with his teacher, was about to design a world in which life would be possible. First of all, he would consider the nature and needs of living organisms, after which he would be in a position to make suggestions about the kinds of atoms which would have to be constructed to fulfil these requirements. Finally, he would be introduced to the chemical elements and would be in a position to appreciate how each one of them fulfils its purpose.

Such an approach would have enormous educational advantages. Biology, chemistry and physics, instead of being taught in isolation, would be seen as a whole. Proceeding along the same lines, unity could very well be achieved with astronomy. At the same time science would appear less impersonal and it would become difficult or impossible for an alienation between science and religion to develop at a later stage.

It needs to be added, perhaps, that a view of chemistry along the lines suggested is in no way a substitute for traditional explanations, where such are available. To discover that there is some purpose in the fact that water expands when it freezes is not to deny the right, indeed the duty, of the chemist to discover the physical reason why this takes place. But pushing back explanations in no way removes the things that need explaining. We may look for casual explanations as far back as we please—and we should certainly do so—but the facts we have marshalled in this chapter seem to show that, ultimately, they must break down. At the back of nature, in the last resort, it is beginning to look as if there must be something much more like a *plan* than the concepts with which science deals.

CHAPTER X

THE LIVING ORGANISM

PRIOR to the rise of evolutionary philosophy in the nineteenth century, the arrangements to be found in the bodies of animals were supposed to afford the strongest of all lines of evidence that nature was designed. It was commonly argued that the muscles, sinews and bones of animals were joined together in a way so ingenious and purposeful, that no thinking person could fail to see that they had been made by God. This theme formed no small part of Paley's well-known *Natural Theology* as well as of several of the famous Bridgewater treatises—that of Sir Charles Bell, on the hand, for example.

After the rise of evolutionary theory from about 1860 onwards, however, the anatomical argument for design was very largely abandoned. The detailed reasons for this change in opinion need not concern us here. But it is important to note that, even for those who accepted Darwin's views, the argument from design had by no means been abolished.

In particular, there was the problem of the creation of life itself. Darwin did not claim that evolution would turn lifeless matter into living. He said only that the principle of natural selection, operating upon almost any organism of moderate complexity, such as a primitive mud fish, might make from it all known animals that inhabit the face of the earth. As to the first problem: Where did the mud fish come from? his words were these: "It is mere rubbish thinking at present of the origin of life; one might as well think of the origin of matter." Nevertheless, Darwin's followers for the most part took it for granted that the spontaneous generation of living matter was a necessary consequence of the evolutionary position and it has been indissolubly connected in the popular mind with evolution ever since.

Looking back it seems strange that scientists and laymen of the past were prepared to accept evolutionary views so readily and so blindly. The simplest cell is overwhelmingly complicated and, before the power of reproduction had been acquired, it is difficult to suppose that natural selection could have created the complex from the simple.

But we must try to understand the earlier point of view. For the nineteenth-century Darwinians, life had none of the mystery that it presents to the modern scientist. The living cell for them was little more complicated than a broom or a chandelier. It consisted of an outer casing or membrane which contained a jelly or viscous fluid. This fluid was christened *protoplasm* and was supposed to constitute the physical basis of life. But, as Sherrington well remarks: "It might perhaps better have been called an unknown quantity. But that would have been less attractive and less intriguing. . . . To call it protoplasm helped to substantialize it."[1]

It was known that within each cell there was a small speck or nucleus together with a few empty holes or vacuoles. These objects seemed of little importance. As for the outer casing, that, too, was simplicity itself—drops of liquids often developed outer membranes of their own accord and it was natural that living matter should do the same!

Not only were cells simple, but so also were the most highly complex organs of the human body. Of these, the human eye attracted, perhaps, more attention than any other. A few simple experiments convinced Helmholtz that the eye, considered as a simple camera, was highly inefficient. It was so bad, indeed, that any instrument maker could have designed a better one.

Despite these defects, however, Helmholtz pointed out that human sight was almost perfect. Helmholtz, like other Darwinians, interpreted this to mean that living matter, as a result of natural selection, possessed an almost quasi-magical power of transcending the tools with which it was endowed. Not that anyone expressed it quite like that—to do so would have been to give the game away—but it was supposed that natural selection had somehow enabled animals to see better and better despite the fact that their badly constructed eyes had long since ceased to improve.

In short, the physical complexity of life was not believed to be of a very high order. And this being so, there were no insuperable

---

[1] *Man on His Nature,* 1940, p. 77. Compare the sensible remark of H. Ward (*Exploring the Universe,* p. 146): "The ultimate analysis of a cell must be as difficult as the analysis of a robin. When you give a common name, protoplasm, to the substance that you find in all cells you are not saying anything."

difficulties in supposing that life might occasionally arise spontaneously.

SYNTHESIS OF LIVING MATTER

Naturally enough, these views encouraged an inevitable spate of experiments designed to produce life in the laboratory. Chemicals which precipitated one another were mixed in colloidal solutions and "chemical gardens" were obtained—said to be most lifelike in character and able to produce all the phenomena of plant life. The chemical vegetation thus formed showed youth and old age; plants budded and reproduced; flowers, mushroom tops, trunks, stems, membranes appeared in wild profusion. Here were the inorganic analogies of life. Here was the proof, if proof were needed, that life was in no way more complex than the colloid chemistry of the metallic silicates.[1]

And if these gardens still lacked something that appertained to the living organism—well—experimenters were not lacking who could show how genuine living organisms could be made from lifeless material. Andrew Crosse first produced his famous *acari* beetles in 1837 by electrolyzing solutions—*Acarus galvanicus,* he called the new species, and his sensational experiments, experiments reproducible (so he said) at will, were accepted for a time in many quarters.[2] Others, such as Bastian, who experimented with brewed concoctions of hay, professed to make new life and made good propaganda of their badly designed experiments, seeking to prove that life was always emerging. And as if to show how omnipresent and commonplace life really was, yet others eagerly pounded meteorites in large mortars and, placing the fragments in culture vessels, produced luxuriant growths of microscopic organisms—organisms that had either been floating about in space for millions of years or had been produced *de novo* since the meteorites fell.

True, the best opinions of the day were never fully satisfied as to the genuineness of these results—especially after the work of Pasteur, who, at the turn of the century, had shown that the classic examples of spontaneous generation were fallacious. Yet the complexity inherent in life was by no means fully realized and many

[1] S. Leduc, *The Mechanism of Life,* Eng. Trans. 1911.

[2] See *Memorials of Andrew Crosse,* 1857.

writers continued to regard the living cell with as much appreciation as an elephant might regard a watch. Even towards the end of
the century, Darwin freely acknowledged that he was itching to
believe Bastian's startling claims, but his critical judgement proved
too strong for him. Chambers, the first all-out evolutionist before
Darwin, was an ardent believer in *Acarus galvanicus*. And we may
be certain that the new generation of materialists wished with all
their hearts that Pasteur had never been born.

STRUCTURE IN NATURE

Such was the nineteenth-century setting. To the materialists of
those days living matter contained few macroscopic and still fewer
microscopic complexities and if, at times, naturalists still marvelled
at the wonderful perfection of the angles in the honeycomb or the
beauty of the snowflake—the labours of a D'Arcy Thomson
eventually showed them that such perfection arose from the
mathematical laws of nature rather than from anything akin to
ingenuity and design.

Certainly there were few who paused to reflect that a system
which allowed of reproduction, of metabolism, of respiration, of
movement and so on, must necessarily be a system of almost
unimaginable complexity. Biologists of the day were content to
take these things for granted and to regard the living cell much as
they might have regarded an extra-pretty crystal or an extra-shiny
drop of a colloidal solution.

Naturally enough, the new philosophy made its devotees almost
impervious to the facts of design in the living organism. Only
occasionally did the obvious macroscopic facts of design in nature
cause men to pause and think. Darwin, for instance, in his *Origin
of Species*, could write:

> It is scarcely possible to avoid comparing the eye with the telescope.
> We know that this instrument has been perfected by the long con-
> tinued efforts of the highest human intellects; and we naturally infer
> that the eye has been formed by a somewhat analogous process. But
> may not this inference be presumptuous? Have we any right to
> assume that the Creator works by intellectual powers like those of
> man?

To this question he returns a negative answer and, as usual, makes the suggestion that the eye is the result of the creative power of natural selection.

Today, perhaps, few would be disposed to deny that natural selection may possess creative power—at least to a very limited degree. But behind the assumption that natural selection can create new and useful structures there lies an assumption to the very existence of which Darwinians were singularly blind even when, like Darwin himself, they were honest enough to admit the difficulty.

GRADUAL IMPROVEMENT

In order to build up a structure by natural selection, it is essential that *each* stage in the building process must make an animal better fitted to its environment than the one before it. An eye that is half developed must be more useful to an animal than an eye that is 49 per cent developed, and this in turn, than one, the development of which has proceeded to only 48 per cent, and so on. The graph of usefulness against the extent of structural organization *must* show a steady upward rise—otherwise progress must inevitably stop, hindered by natural selection itself. If the graph is not a steady upward rise, but has ups and downs, then natural selection (which selects usefulness and adaptation), working from *either* direction, will force the organism to the nearest maximum.

Today, with our much greater knowledge of and familiarity with complex systems, we know that steady upward rises of the kind demanded by materialistic evolutionists are unknown to science. Isolated fundamental changes make a machine less efficient than it was before and may even make it useless, unless, indeed, numerous other adaptations are made at the same time. The radio manufacturer cannot turn one model of a wireless set into a larger and better one by continuous stages—he cannot add a new valve, a condenser, a piece of wire, etc., in a series of operations, and hope each time to obtain a model that is slightly better than the one before. All the changes must be made at once—or not at all! To add an extra valve to a wireless set you must first cut through wires, disconnect the loudspeaker, etc., and at once the set becomes useless as a functioning whole. Only after passing through the *useless* stage can it be made more useful than before. It is the same with all arrangements of matter organized as functioning units. To ask for a gradual, uniform, improvement is, it seems, to ask for the impossible.

Now many biologists have long suspected that precisely the same principle applies to nature. If it is desired to develop one organ from another the intermediate stages will, in general, be useless and so will have no survival value. The evidence of this is even more conclusive when we consider habits rather than organs. Fabre, for instance, was convinced that many of the habits of insects could never have arisen by natural selection. And the changes which are necessary if a symbiotic union is to develop between two species which, in the process, become mutually useful to one another, are such that a change in one species which did not take place simultaneously with an appropriate change in the other would achieve no useful purpose.

This difficulty, recognized by Darwin, makes it difficult to entertain the view that an undirected evolution can progressively make simple things more complex. It was confidently hoped in the nineteenth century that further progress would throw light upon the matter. It has certainly done so—but not in the sense that the Darwinians had hoped. Today evidence is accumulating that the difficulty is universal and it has been found to confront us even in the simplest imaginable instances where the complexities and alternative explanations that have in the past been suggested as ways of evasion do not enter the picture.

The evidence provided by modern studies in genetics is here of peculiar interest. The mould *Neurospora* (commonly used in such experiments) manufactures the amino-acid arginine and it is known that at least seven stages are involved in the synthesis of this substance. Each of these stages is dependent upon the presence of an enzyme and each enzyme in turn depends upon the presence of a particular gene in the hereditary substance of the mould.

Now some at least, if not all, of the intermediate stages involve the production of products, such as ornithine and citrulline, which are believed to be quite useless to the mould—they are not known to serve a useful purpose in any other living organism and they are not essential building bricks in the manufacture of proteins.

Thus all the details are known of a long many-staged synthesis, each step of which requires the presence of a particular elaborately organized enzyme molecule which can carry out a particular reaction.

How did all these enzymes and the genes which make them arise? They cannot arise by gradual evolution, step by step, for when once an organism develops an unnecessary product, natural selection will tend to eliminate that product. No likely mechanism has ever been suggested.

The orthodox reply to this point is that useless genes are often linked with useful ones. So a favourable mutation in one direction can carry along with it, so to speak, the unfavourable mutations of another gene which are the necessary preliminaries for the emergence of something new and better.

Of course this might, and doubtless does, happen now and then by chance. But as a general explanation it carries no conviction: rather the reverse. Useless random changes can take place in a multitude of directions—what is there to ensure that those will be preserved which, considered in the light of *subsequent* evolutionary history, will be seen to have been useful? Besides, it is difficult to suppose that natural selection is much of a creative power if favourable mutations are bogged down by linkage with unfavourable ones. Though many biologists pay lip service to the linkage theory, many are discreetly silent and it is difficult to believe that any think of it as other than a somewhat desperate expedient. But there is worse to follow.

SIZE

A consideration of elementary scientific principles leads to yet a further difficulty. Galileo realized, centuries ago, that mechanisms must have an optimum size, and his principle still holds good and forms part of our scientific heritage. One cannot simply imitate a small machine on a much larger or much smaller scale. There comes a point at which basic redesign is called for—the penalty being immense inefficiency.

The reason for this is that weight, which is proportional to volume, increases as the *cube* of dimensions, but surface area increases only as the square. The force which can be generated in a muscle or tendon depends upon cross section and therefore upon area, and is otherwise limited by the ultimate chemical forces between atoms. But the work required to, say, lift a land animal, will depend upon its weight. So a fly enlarged to the size of a dog will break its legs. Surface area also determines such factors as the rate at which heat can be lost and the rate of loss or gain of carbon dioxide or oxygen through membranes. But, once more, if the structure of a small animal is repeated on a larger scale, the heat which must be lost or the gases which must diffuse, will depend upon the body weight, and this increases much faster than the surface area available. So the fly the size of a dog will be unable to respire, and, even if it manages to do so, it will get too hot.

So if we imagine evolution as starting with small organized structures there must come a time when, as a result of mere size increase, small naturally selected modifications will no longer prove useful. A radically new design of the organism will be called for. But, by its very nature, natural selection cannot provide for this. It can only modify what already exists: it cannot effect radical redesign.

The point is well illustrated by comparing the young of a species with the adults. Of necessity (except in the relatively uncommon cases where metamorphosis takes place) young and old are built upon the same basic plan. If natural selection could so modify the young that they would, from the start, be free living creatures, able to fend for themselves, it would doubtless have done so. But we find instead that the young must always be shielded—either inside or outside the mother's body—because they are unable to fend for themselves until they reach a certain critical size.

It seems necessary to conclude that, whatever may be the creative powers that lie dormant in the principle of natural selection, there are limits beyond which they cannot go. It is misleading and untrue, then, to argue that since Darwin's day the argument from design based upon the structure of animals has lost its force. This is certainly not the case. Indeed, the argument has been greatly strengthened as a result of our much increased knowledge concerning the intricacies and wonders of organic design.

ORIGIN OF LIFE[1]

It is time to say something about the origin of life. Materialistic writers, copying one another, say that before life arrived on earth,

[1] See A. I. Oparin, *The Origin of Life*, 1938 and 1956; B. Beutner, *Life's Beginnings on the Earth*, 1939; N. H. Horowitz, *Proc. National Acad. Sciences*, 1945, **31**, 153; J. Alexander, *Life: Its Nature and Origin*, 1948, W. E. Swinton, *The Corridor of Life*, 1948; J. D. Bernal, *Proc. Physical Soc.*, 1949; *The Physical Basis of Life*, 1951; *The Origin of Life*, New Biology No. 16 (Penguin Books) 1954; S. W. Fox, *Jour. Chem.*

the chemical environment had become exceedingly complex—as thick as soup, as Haldane used to say—so that the first living organisms had no need to synthesize more than one or two of the many chemical compounds they required. In time an early organism used up one of the chemical substances present, until there was none left. The organism was about to perish, but just in the nick of time a few survivors mutated into a form which was able to use one of the other compounds present and to turn it into the first. Again, the second chemical was used up and the new organism again mutated and learned how to use a third. And so on. At each new mutation a new gene was added, the organism became more complex and was enabled to carry out increasingly complex and lengthy chemical syntheses. (Horowitz.)

What is to be said of this picture? Firstly, there is the supposed complex chemical environment with which it starts. Oparin argued that if oxygen has been in excess, organic compounds could never have formed. Accordingly, he made the novel suggestion that the early atmosphere contained free hydrogen and hydrocarbons which, under the influence of lightning flashes, gave rise to ammonia, more complex compounds being built up under the influence of sunlight in the course of time.

Oparin's views, apparently, stimulated the Russian school of astronomers to produce the new model of the earth's formation which we have already noted. By supposing that the earth was *cold* at the beginning, the difficulty of the escape of hydrogen was lessened. By supposing that a stationary zone of great cold exists in the stratosphere, it was argued that very little water would get high enough for decomposition and consequent loss of hydrogen. (Subsequent calculations, however, have shown that in view of the turbulence of the upper atmosphere, water would enter the upper regions in great abundance, despite a low-temperature barrier, and free oxygen would form rapidly as hydrogen escaped into space.) Oparin's views have been ably defended in the West by Urey. Though it is impossible to be sure, it seems unlikely that they will survive for, as we shall see shortly, the primary reason for their existence seems to have disappeared.

Education, 1957, **34**, 472. For the best modern review of the subject see R. J. C. Harris, *The Origin of Life* Transactions of the Victoria Institute, 1949, **81**, 58. A wealth of interesting material will also be found in *Proceedings of the First International Symposium on the Origin of Life on the Earth*, Moscow, 1957 (English Ed. Pergamon Press, 1959).

Oparin's views at first received scant respect in the West. A leading authority dismissed them with the remark, "The astrophysical data on which Oparin has based his speculations are largely obsolete and often incorrectly interpreted."[1] That steam was present in the atmosphere in the earth's earliest ages can hardly be doubted and steam itself, by the action of both heat, light and radiation must have decomposed to give free oxygen and hydrogen, the latter escaping into space. The theory that the earth was once covered with a reducing atmosphere, in which complex organic substances might have been built up over long ages was then, and still is, difficult to square with existing knowledge.

Thus it is pointed out that even in the earliest rocks, there are vast deposits of *ferric* oxide (the *higher* oxide of iron) and of calcium sulphate (showing that much sulphur was oxidized). These could not have formed in a reducing atmosphere. The fact that helium is absent and neon rare (though both gases are cosmically abundant) confirms the view that the still lighter hydrogen would rapidly have escaped into space, owing to the lack of sufficient gravitational pull. A critical survey of a wide range of evidence leads Rubey to conclude: "It seems likely that oxygen has been accumulating from the photo-dissociation of water vapour ever since the Earth was formed."[2] In short, only planets much larger than the Earth are likely to have reducing atmospheres.

A new line was given to the argument about the origin of life in 1955 when Stanley Miller in Los Angeles announced that he had sparked a mixture of methane, ammonia, water and hydrogen and had obtained a complex mixture in which several amino-acids were detectable. The gas mixture used was supposed to correspond to the reducing atmosphere of the primitive earth. Later, the same

[1] R. Wildt, *Reviews of Modern Physics*, 1942, **14,** 151.

[2] W. W. Rubey, in *Developments of the Hydrosphere and Atmosphere* . . . Geol. Soc. of America, Special Papers, No. 62, 1955. Rubey points out that fossilized carbon in the ground is equivalent in amount to the oxygen in our atmosphere. Vast supplies of oxygen must, therefore, have been available to oxidize iron, sulphur and carbon (to form iron oxides, sulphates and carbonates) *before* photosynthesis commenced.

Similar views are expressed by V. M. Goldsmidt, *Geochemistry*, Oxford, 1954, p. 509; R. T. Chamberlin, in *Atmospheres of the Earth and Planets*, Ed. by G. P. Kuiper, Chap. 8, etc. For the opposite view, see, for example, H. C. Urey, *The Planets, their Origin and Development*, Yale, 1952. But Urey has since modified his views—see *Moscow Symposium*.

result was recorded when a similar mixture was subjected to bombardment by radioactive substances.

These results could only be obtained in a reducing atmosphere. When oxygen was present in excess, no organic compounds were produced. But in 1957 it was shown that a massive dose of *gamma* radiation produced traces of amino-acids, amongst other things, from ammonium carbonate (i.e. ammonia and carbon dioxide).

In its early days the earth was much more radioactive than now. Ammonia was doubtless formed locally, at times, from metallic nitrides and water, while carbon dioxide was available in the atmosphere. The experiments mentioned, in which massive quantities of starting materials were employed, gave only micrograms of amino-acids. Moreover, electric discharges and *gamma* radiation destroy amino-acids as well as make them. So at best their concentration would only have been excessively small. However, it is reasonable enough to suppose that minute quantities of amino-acids would have been formed, mixed, of course, with thousands of other products, in early seas and lakes. And this would apply whatever view we take about the state of the early atmosphere.

It is often argued that the concentration of these organic compounds would have increased locally as a result of evaporation in pools and lagoons. But this is far from evident. Most of the organic matter would be decomposed by the very same radiation that made it. If a little survived in shady spots, then mixtures of organic compounds would soon react together to give insoluble precipitates which would rapidly be removed from the scene of further action—for reactions cease in the solid state. Oparin seems to realize this difficulty but suggests that the precipitated insoluble particles (coacervates) would not settle out. In view of the prevalence of inorganic salts and the great variety of products formed this supposition is very doubtful.

Modern experiments are done under idealized conditions—starting with pure chemicals which do not occur as such in nature. Even so, yields are measured in millionth parts of a gram. We may picture, if we like, early stagnant pools containing minute traces of thousands of compounds formed as a result of radioactive bombardments. And doubtless the simpler amino-acids would be there too. But it is not a promising beginning.

The simplest imaginable form of "life"—a self-duplicating

mechanism, like a part of a chromosome—would not require amino-acids but a nucleic acid built from a phosphate, the sugar ribose or desoxyribose, a suitable purine and a pyrimidine. None of these compounds are known to be formed from electric sparks or radiation on common substances—though it is conceivable that a few such molecules might be formed.

TOXICOLOGY AND ANTI-VITAMINS

The idea that life started spontaneously in a complex mixture of chemical compounds formed by natural means leads to further difficulties which are commonly overlooked. Before discussing these we must say something about the ability of organisms to withstand poisons.

Few branches of science are more amazing in the wonders they disclose than the rapidly developing science of *immuno-chemistry*. Of tens of millions of alien proteins, introduced into the bloodstream, each one possesses the power to generate a chemical which will react with and destroy it.

Toxicology reveals a state of affairs that is hardly less surprising. With a wisdom that is almost unerring, the body seems to know just how to deal with every one of thousands upon thousands of simple toxic substances that may enter the system. And in each instance the compound is altered in some way—oxidized, reduced, made into a methyl or benzyl derivative and so on—until a material is produced which is no longer toxic, and this is then quietly excreted.

Uncanny wisdom it seems indeed! And yet it is not uncanny and it is not wisdom. The body is functioning simply as a wonderfully designed mechanism—though of the details of this mechanism very little is known. But wonderful as the mechanism is, it is not infallible. At times molecules—perhaps generated by some foreign organisms—may enter the vastly complex array of interacting substances in the cells and, because of their resemblance to some molecule which is natural and essential to the body's mechanism, may, so to speak, clog the wheels and impede the subsequent reactions upon which life depends. For the body is a system so complex, so highly co-ordinated, that the smallest disturbances in its dynamic equilibrium may prevent its proper functioning. It is in this way that we are learning to regard disease and poisoning—

the wonder being not that these things occur but that they occur so rarely.

With these few comments we may introduce the anti-vitamins—substances that have been much in the limelight of late years. Very small changes in the molecules of vitamins (for instance, in pantothenic or para-aminobenzoic acids) result in the formation of potent poisons which function simply by imitating the parent vitamin. For the similarity in shape and properties is such that natural mechanisms react with these compounds to produce substances which, at a later stage, are useless to the organism.

Now evidence is accumulating that anti-vitamins often occur naturally and that some of the potent natural poisons (the toxins, for instance) owe their properties to this cause. Nature, in short, shows no tendency to produce vitamins rather than anti-vitamins. And this is precisely as we should expect—for chemically the one set of compounds are neither more nor less stable than the other.

If then, we could imagine a complex group of molecules being formed by chance at the time that life first came upon the earth, we must face the fact that anti-vitamins would have been formed as well as vitamins: molecules to make life impossible as well as those to make it possible. We must not forget that a biological system of great complexity is easily put out of gear by a very few molecules of the wrong kind—a million combinations that are right and workable become useless if one happens to be unfortunate. And, of course, with the first living organisms, there would have been no time for the evolution of immuno-chemical and toxicological mechanisms to prevent harmful molecules from destroying life as soon as it came into existence. In short, the prospect of a living cell coming into existence by chance seems more remote the more we consider what such an event would have involved.

Not only have all materialist writers who hold that life arose spontaneously ignored the existence of anti-vitamins, but they have ignored also most of the more obvious characteristics of living matter. Oparin, for instance, shows little or no appreciation of what a living cell must accomplish in order that it may live. He is content when he has drawn attention to the most superficial resemblances.

FREE ENERGY

From the lowliest organism and up through the scale to man, one thing necessary for life is a supply of free energy—energy, that is to say, which is available for doing work and has not been lost as heat. Such energy is required for all vital functions—for energizing cilia, flagellæ and muscles, for working glands, for pumping fluids against osmotic pressure, for manufacturing new molecules, for reproduction, for growth, for metabolism, for making light in luminous organs or electricity in electric organs, and so on.

Throughout the whole realm of nature energy is derived from the oxidation of sugar (glucose). This substance is converted (or "burnt") to water and carbon dioxide. Now in all ordinary chemical reactions which evolve heat, the energy is simply lost. Only rarely can energy be reconverted from heat to a usable form and, even then, elaborate machinery (boilers, turbines, etc.) is necessary. But in order to live at all, the simplest cell must accomplish what man can only achieve with fire and steam. For the cell must obtain energy and deliver it where and when it is needed— and this it does with efficiencies which are believed to range even up to 70 per cent, though 35 per cent would be a good performance for a power station using superheated steam.

Details of the mechanism employed in nature cannot detain us here—they will be found in modern works on biochemistry. But there are certain points about the mechanism which are so important and so striking that they provide strong evidence that life did not arise spontaneously. In the first place—except for the last stage which determines how the energy is to be used—the same mechanism is employed in the most primitive and the most complex organisms. Despite the enormous complexity of this mechanism, we can find no evidence of its development or evolution. Indeed, such evolution as there has been is in the reverse order. In the yeast cell, for example, which thrives in absence of oxygen, a part of the mechanism remains intact while the rest has evidently been lost. Similar instances are by no means uncommon. It appears that when cells or organisms have lived for a long time in surroundings which provide them with ready-made materials, they lose the power to make these and, once lost, the power is not regained.

Nature stores energy in the form of a remarkable substance, found, as far as is known, in every living cell and known as ATP (adenosine triphosphate, synthesized in 1948). The breakdown of glucose to carbon dioxide and water involves about twenty stages and in these, whenever energy is liberated, it is stored as ATP. Every one of these stages depends upon the presence of an enzyme (all enzymes are proteins with exceedingly complex molecules) and generally a co-enzyme is also necessary. Before the process can commence, therefore, at least some forty special kinds of molecules, all of them complex and many excessively so, must be present— and allowing for substances not yet known a truer estimate may be 100–200.

In the first living cell each of these substances must have been present in sufficient concentration to be effective and, to prevent diffusion, they must, therefore, have been enclosed in a cell wall.

Such a system must work as a whole—one stage following another. If a single stage is missing, the whole system is useless. Certain poisons (prussic acid, mustard gas, etc.), destroy life because they prevent a *single* enzyme functioning. So the system cannot develop by stages—to be effective, it must all come into existence at the same time.

The spontaneous generation of so great a degree of complexity would be inconceivable enough—but the difficulties have scarcely begun. Not only have we to suppose that all the necessary molecules, each of great complexity, were formed by chance within a minute volume enclosed by a cell wall but that they were formed in total absence of closely similar molecules which, if they were present, would have functioned as anti-vitamins. Then again, we must bear in mind that many of the necessary compounds (especially the co-enzymes) are exceedingly unstable and, once formed, would have disappeared in half an hour. So it will not do to suggest that they might be formed one by one by chance—with long periods in between. Chance must produce all the molecules that are required, concentrated together in a cell, within a matter of at most an hour or so.

Even this does not bring us to an end of our difficulties. For, let us imagine that the long arm of coincidence did, just once shall we say, in the whole history of the earth, overcome all those difficulties and did produce the right molecules in a cell that was formed by chance—the cell would still be incapable of life for it would still be unable to obtain energy from glucose.

The reason is this. The early stages of the breakdown of glucose actually use up ATP. Not until a series of six enzyme reactions have taken place is the ATP remade—in the end much more is made than was previously consumed. The living cell, in fact, presents us with a state of affairs which Malcolm Dixon, one of the greatest living authorities on enzymes, has compared to a factory designed to produce machine tools. Without machine tools the factory cannot even start production of machine tools—no matter how perfect its organization.

The same situation confronts us in connexion with the nucleic acid spiral. (See p. 111). Even if we are provided with nucleic acid, it will not spontaneously turn into the double helix upon which life and reproduction depends. A specialized enzyme is necessary for this to happen and the enzyme is a protein. But the helix re-creates this protein at a later stage—though by a very roundabout mechanism. Again it is like the machine tool which makes machine tools but does not come into existence without machine tools.

In fact all enzymes are made only by enzymes or their nucleic acid percursors. Given enzymes we may hope to understand how new ones arise. But, "If enzymes are formed only by enzymes, how were the first enzymes formed?" In short, "to say, airily, as some do, that whenever the conditions are suitable for life to exist, life will inevitably emerge, is to betray a complete ignorance of the problems involved."[1]

The difficulties seem at last to be dimly realized by those who, undaunted, propagate materialistic viewpoints. Thus J. D. Bernal, who was in the chair at a B.B.C. Broadcast on the subject of the "Origin of Life" (March 9, 1958), at which many hypotheses were suggested and the difficulties for the better part ignored, ended with the confession: "It would have been much easier to discuss how life didn't originate than how it did."

In short, far from finding evidences of the operation of chance or of known materialistic laws we repeatedly encounter, instead, wonderfully ingenious molecular machinery that becomes, as Ubbelohde[2] well remarks, more and more unintelligible to our

[1] M. Dixon and E. C. Webb, *Enzymes*, 1958, p. 666.

[2] A. R. J. P. Ubbelohde, *Time and Thermodynamics*, 1947, p. 96.

minds except in terms of analogy with human invention and human ingenuity.

COMPLEXITY OF THE CELL

Much more might be said. The production of ATP itself depends upon a remarkable property of the element phosphorus (see p. 116)—for the phosphate group in combining with itself stores energy which balances that lost in some of the fundamental breakdown processes of the glucose molecule. Again, muscles employ an ingenious mechanism for obtaining energy temporarily when the supply of ATP runs short. Then again, the complexity of a living cell must be vastly greater than we have depicted it—for mechanisms must be present for utilizing the ATP for many purposes, including the continuous synthesis of all (or nearly all) the enzymes and co-enzymes which are often more or less short-lived.

More exciting still are the prospects ahead. Now that the basic structure of the chromosome units has at last been discovered, the question arises, How is it that the genes direct the synthesis of the enzymes? Every cell in our bodies contains these spiral structures —forty-six chromosomes in man, and each a mile or two long when we make a model in which the average distance between the atoms is represented by an inch. Of this we still know little. But it seems as if a fundamental repeating distance which determines the spacing between coils in the spirals is the same as the fundamental repeating distance in the amino-acid spirals. If so, the properties of the phosphorus atom must be exactly in step with that of nitrogen and carbon.

Although all the cells in the body contain the spirals, the enormous mass of information which these contain can only partly be made use of in each anatomical situation. It is as if the individual cells which constitute a foot, a finger, or an eye, know which pages to consult in order to make themselves. All the other information available remains in hiding. How is this done? We do not know. It is clear that wonderful and ingenious mechanisms must be enshrined. As cells divide in embryological growth, they become increasingly differentiated—they learn more and more about which pages to keep open and which to ignore.

What the biologist calls *genes* are regions in the spiral which contain special codes. Each gene corresponds to an enzyme which it brings into existence. And the enzymes, like the genes, are over-whelmingly complex.

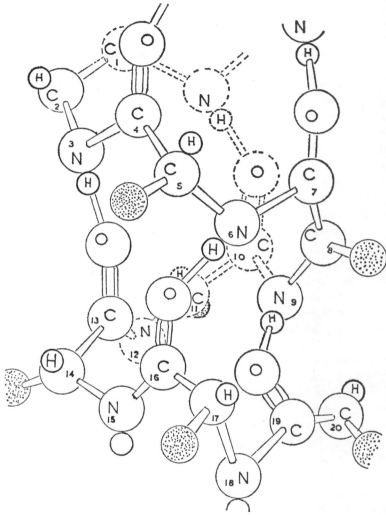

FIG. 9. PROTEIN SPIRAL.

In proteins the amino-acid residues—CO. CHR. NH—are commonly joined in chains. In many proteins the chains form a spiral with about 3·7 units per turn. Such a spiral is illustrated above. It will be noted that each N is linked, through a hydrogen bond, to the O below it. The spiral nature of the molecule will be apparent if the atoms in the chain, marked 1, 2, 3, 4, etc., are followed through the diagram. The shaded spheres represent the radicals R of which 20 varieties are present in proteins.

THE LIVING ORGANISM 137

The picture of the cell which we possess today differs greatly from views which were once entertained. All the earlier materialists held to the view that living matter was quite simple in structure. And until recently it was almost universally held that large units like proteins were built up by seemingly endless repeats of basically simple patterns.

The opposite has, however, turned out to be the case. Sanger (Nobel Prize, 1958) showed that there are no repeat patterns at all in the molecule of insulin, and the same applies to other proteins since investigated. In 1958 Kendrew and his co-workers in Cambridge were able for the first time to prepare a three-dimensional picture of a protein by X-ray analysis.

The protein chosen for this work, because of its relative simplicity (153 amino-acid residues), was *myoglobin*—an oxygen-carrying material found in large amounts in sea mammals. The molecule contains an iron atom surrounded by the usual four pyrrole rings, forming a small flat plate. This is tucked away inside a series of coils of great complexity and is, except on one side (where oxygen attaches itself) almost hidden from view. "Perhaps the most remarkable features of the molecule are its complexity and lack of symmetry. The arrangement seems to be almost totally lacking in the kind of regularities which one would instinctively anticipate, and it is more complicated than has been predicted by

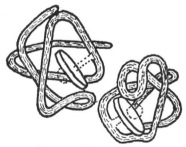

FIG. 10. HAEMOGLOBIN.

Diagram showing two of the four units which together make up the haemoglobin molecule. The snake-like objects are each formed from about 150 amino-acid residues linked in spiral fashion as shown in Fig. 9. At one point on each chain these are attached (by a histidine link) to form plate-shaped haem units which consist essentially of an iron atom surrounded by four pyrrole rings. Oxygen molecules attach themselves to the reverse side of these plates in the positions marked by circles of dots. The whole molecule, with the four units neatly fitting into one another, is ball-shaped. (After Perutz *et al* 1960, adapted.)

any theory of protein structure."[1] More recent work has shown that the same basic structure, repeated (not exactly) four times over occurs in haemoglobin.

No wonder that the miracle of the cell fascinates everyone who has given it a thought. Sherrington describes it in language that is romantic. "It is a scene of energy-cycles, suites of oxidation and reduction, concatenated ferment-actions. It is like a magic hive the walls of whose chambered spongework are shifting veils of ordered molecules, and rend and renew as operations rise and cease. A world of surfaces and streams. We seem to watch battalions of specific catalysts, like Maxwell's 'demons', lined up, each waiting stop-watch in hand, for its moment to play the part assigned to it, a step in one or other great thousand-linked chain process." More recently Dr. Stuart Mudd has written: "Cells of many kinds of bacteria, furnished only with water, salts, glucose and simple sources of carbon and nitrogen, can synthesize proteins, complex carbohydrates, lipids, ribose and desoxyribose nucleic acids, growth accessories and enzymes, all organized into characteristic and reproducible protoplasmic systems. The cell can reproduce itself and divide within an hour at body temperature. These feats of chemical synthesis and organization which cannot be duplicated by the finest chemical laboratories in existence, are accomplished within a cell a few microns in length and less than half a micron in diameter. The plain facts would seem fantastic if they were not so familiar. The simultaneous occurrence of the complex reactions involving energy utilization, synthesis and organization of the materials elaborated implies means of keeping the reactions in proper temporal and spatial relation to each other, and implies organization equivalent to an efficient system of transport and logistics."[2]

In 1933 James Gray summarized the situation by asking: "Why, then, should we accept the spontaneous origin of living matter? It is possible, but it is so improbable that, if considered as an observable phenomenon, in any other sphere of human thought it would be discarded as a figment of a deranged brain. . . . Is there any evidence which suggests that, within the physical world, a dynamic machine has come into existence? . . . Unless a positive answer can be given to this question, the belief in the spontaneous origin of

[1] Kendrew, et al, Nature, 1958, **181**, 662.

[2] Sir Charles Sherrington, Man on his Nature, 1940, p. 78 (Quoted by courtesy of the Syndics of the Cambridge University Press); S. Mudd, Nature, 1948, **161**, 302.

living matter seems to be a negation of the principles which underlie scientific thought."[1]

Today vastly more is known about the complexities of cell mechanisms than was known in 1933 and the difficulties involved in the theory that life arose spontaneously are correspondingly greater.

How, then, we may ask *did* life come into existence. It would seem that only two answers are logically possible. The most natural one is that suggested (not, of course, for the first time) by Dr. V. H. Mottram.

"It looks as though an intelligent purposeful mind must have stepped in when matter on earth had cooled sufficiently, and created proteins and endowed them with life."[2]

Another possibility is that, despite all that has been said, life really *did* originate spontaneously from matter without the intervention of intelligence. It is impossible finally to dispose of such a view. But it is important to realize what this view entails. It means that in the chemical atoms there are wonderful powers and complexities, of the type we dealt with in the last chapter, but far more subtle and complex. They must be powers and properties of which, thus far, no inkling of independent evidence has been forthcoming. We must suppose that the atoms have the power, unaided, to build themselves up into vastly complex structures—complex in the true sense of the word (i.e. not by repetition of smaller units). They must be naturally endowed with powers to avoid at least most of the million and one possible pitfalls which would end in failure. And they must do it quickly for geological time of a few thousand million years, though seemingly long to us, is in fact microscopically small when we are thinking of structures which *could* have been built up (mostly uselessly) not in mere thousands of millions of ways, but in perhaps ten raised to the power of thousands of millions.

In fact, according to this view, atoms and molecules must shake down into organic structures in much the same way as they form crystals. This view, as Pantin has reminded us, was that held before

[1] Professor James Gray, *Presidential Address to Section D* (Zoology), *of the British Association*, 1933.

[2] *The Listener*, April 22, 1948. J. L. Baldwin has recently made the interesting suggestion that the early forms of life, thus created, were not genetically simple but contained all the complexities which have subsequently unfolded or *evolved* (the *correct* usage of this much misused word) in subsequent history (*New Answer to Darwinism*, 1957).

Darwin's day—by Richard Owen, for example. It was reasonable enough in the nineteenth century when organisms were supposed to be fairly simple. But modern research has made it less plausible.

However, if this view is true, then the planning and wonder lying unseen at the back (so to speak) of the universe must be even more staggering in its immensity than anything which a special creationist has envisaged.

It *may* be so. We should never shut our eyes to scientific evidence or reasonable suggestions to the effect that it *is* so. But when those whose only object seems to be to support atheism, pour out hundreds of pages, of which the excerpts below are typical, we may be forgiven for feeling unimpressed.

> Darwin proved that purposefulness was not mystical and super-natural. (p. 350). Natural selection started in thermodynamically open systems, consisting of coacervates. There was "a gradual increase in the amount of material organized in the system". "The only systems which were preserved for further evolution were those which were most highly developed." [Still not alive!] They "became more dynamic" and were later "capable of self-preservation and growth". Final conclusion (p. 487), "Life, as one of the forms of the motions of matter, must [*sic.*] arise every time suitable conditions for it occur at any place in the universe." [A remarkable logic this, in which a thousand *just possibles, mights* and *perhaps's* lead in the end to a *"must"*.][1]

> For much more on the same lines the Moscow *Symposium* may be consulted.

[1] From A. I. Oparin, *The Origin of Life on the Earth*, Eng. Trans., 1957.

CHAPTER XI

NATURE—THE FIRST INVENTOR

"Go, from the creatures thy instruction take,
Learn from the birds what foods the thickets yield;
Learn from the beasts the physic of the field;
The art of building from the bee receive;
Learn of the mole to plough, the worm to weave;
Learn of the little nautilus to sail,
Spread the thin oar, and catch the driving gale."

Pope.

DESIGN—or at least an *appearance* of design—runs like a silver thread through every main branch of science. We have seen evidences of its presence in physics, in astronomy, in chemistry and in biology. It confronts us no matter what part of nature it is that we examine—whether it be the remote nebulae, small organisms under the microscope or the atoms of chemistry.

How seriously can we take this appearance of design? Should we indeed speak of it as design at all? Are we merely tending to clothe nature with human images: to see in her a reflection of our own minds?

Suggestions of this kind have been made often enough, especially in recent years. But it would seem that their truth or otherwise can be subjected to a very simple test.

No one doubts that it is right to say that the inventions of men are the results of design—no one supposes that such a statement can be explained away completely by saying that we tend to see egotistical self-reflections of our own minds when we think of the inventions of others.

How far can the analogy be pressed? Is the design which we find in nature of the same kind as the design which we find in science and in technology? Or are there differences which would make any argument based on an analogy between them suspect?

The answer is, undoubtedly, that they are of the same kind. For man's greatest inventions quite often turn out to be adaptations—

sometimes even copies—of what he finds in nature. In this chapter we shall consider some of the evidence for this statement.

FAMILIAR INVENTIONS

Everyone knows that many of the simple devices we use in everyday life have their counterparts in nature. Lever systems, such as those we use in scissors and pincers, are extremely common in the anatomy of vertebrates and are seen to perfection in the claws of crabs. The lubrication of machinery has its counterpart in the lubrication which we find in connexion with all moving parts in nature, in addition to the lubrication on the surfaces of animals such as slugs and fishes. The syringe works on the principle found in the nematocyst of the hydra. Modern gliding depends for its success upon picking out the rising currents of air, a trick used by the gossamer spider, and by the pterodactyl in ancient times. Streamlining, again, is a principle used in birds, insects and fishes. And most people know that the release of atomic energy first achieved

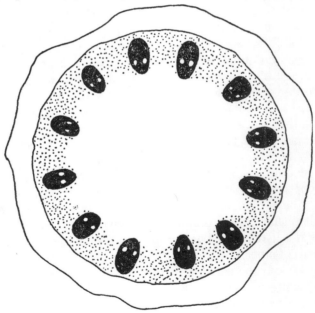

FIG. 11.

Diagram of a section of a typical stem (monocotyledonous) showing vascular bundles consisting partly of wood embedded in soft connective tissue. The vascular bundles take the tension, the connective tissue being under compression.

by man in 1945 has long had its counterpart in the sun and in the stars.

Indeed, even the idea of aerial flight seems to have originated from the flight of birds. "A bird," says Leonardo da Vinci in the *Codice Atlanto*, "is an instrument working according to mathematical law, an instrument which it is within the capacity of man to reproduce with all its movements."[1] And a modern writer remarks: "It is doubtful whether man would ever have conceived flight had nature not provided the pattern."[2]

Turning to more detailed systems, present practices in the construction of engineering structures—bridges, towers, cranes, aero-

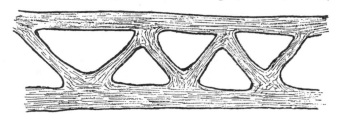

FIG. 12.

Diagram to show the general appearance of a section through the metacarpal bone from a vulture's wing. The resemblance to an engineering truss is obvious, but the wing is better designed than the truss, since the struts are not confined to one plane. (*After Prochnow.*)

planes and so on, find almost exact counterparts in nature. In rushes, in straw and in the bones of birds we find that maximum strength is obtained by the use of a hollow stem or tube which enables the plant or bone to withstand lateral pressure. In the same way, hollow tubes are often used in engineering (as in the bicycle) in order to withstand bending.

In plants, while this device is used, other principles are also employed. In the simplest form the hollow stem is built of two parts—bundles of strong fibres which weight for weight may withstand as much tension as steel and weak filling material which is "blown out" with small air spaces and able to withstand compression. When a reed bends in the wind, the tensile strength of the fibres is used on one side and the compressive strength of the light binding material on the other.

[1] See *Studies and Essays in the History of Science and Learning*, dedicated to George Sarton, Ed. M. F. A. Montagu, 105–10.

[2] M. J. B. C. Davy, *Nature*, 1950, **165**, 825

The same principle is widely used in engineering. In the wing of an aeroplane, for instance, the metal struts may take the tensile stresses while some light material, such as balsa wood, may be used to withstand compression. In nature (as in the palm tree) fibres often inter-cross as if they were following stress lines—and precisely the same principle (the geodesic principle) is widely applied to the construction of the wings of aircraft. The modern age has dawned because man has learned how to duplicate complex shapes and patterns, again and again, infallibly, effortlessly and almost endlessly. Every prototype demands careful thought and attention to myriads of trivial details; after that automation takes over. Painfully we have learned the value of the "unit process"—the fact that, in general each single alteration or addition to a partly completed object can be performed most efficiently by doing one thing at a time : "a complicated process must be split into a sequence of individual operations, each of which may be performed in a piece of equipment specially designed to carry out the unit operation."[1]

Again, these are the methods of nature. Enzymes are nature's "unit process" machine tools. Sir George Thomson reminds us that our machine age is foreshadowed by nature. "Henry Ford may have thought that he was initiating something new when he gave us mass production in its most characteristic form, but he was merely a humble imitator of nature."[2]

MAN THE IMITATOR

Engineers have often deliberately copied the constructional methods of nature. Thus "stiffeners" corresponding precisely to those found in plants were used in the great twelve-foot-diameter diagonal struts of the Forth Bridge, while the tendency to "buckle" was resisted, as in the jointed stem of the bamboo, by the use of "stiffener rings"—diaphragms set twenty feet apart within the tube.

Another instance is afforded by Joseph Paxton's design of the Crystal Palace for the Great Exhibition of 1850. Paxton had been in charge of the Duke of Devonshire's gardens. There he had built

[1] E. J. Stephens, *Chemistry and Industry*, August 28, 1948, p. 551.

[2] Sir George P. Thomson, "Atomicity and Patterns", *Journ. Washington Acad. of Science*, 1956, **46**, 201.

a novel greenhouse to house the rapidly growing Victoria Regina lily, and in it deliberately copied the methods used in the huge leaves of the lily itself. Later, he applied the same principles to the Crystal Palace building—"Nature was the engineer," he said, "Nature had provided the leaf with longitudinal and transverse girders and supports that I, borrowing from it, have adopted in this building".[1] It was humorously stated of Paxton at the time that he had "floated to fame on a lily leaf."

The construction of bones is peculiarly interesting. Thus the two main bones of the leg (*tibia* and *fibia*) have large heads but become narrower lower down. To economize weight, it is desirable that the forces applied to the head should be transmitted evenly to the thin part of the bone below. Inside the bone is a fine network of bony fibres (the *cancellous tissue*) running through the marrow, blood vessels, etc. Some of these minute trabeculæ of bone run in curving lines from the head to the hollow shaft of the bone. This system is intercrossed by another set at right angles to the first and it is known that these bony fibres follow the lines of tension and compression in the bones and that it is due to their existence that

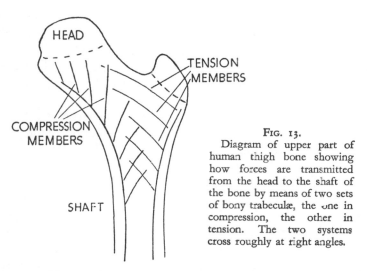

FIG. 13.
Diagram of upper part of human thigh bone showing how forces are transmitted from the head to the shaft of the bone by means of two sets of bony trabeculæ, the one in compression, the other in tension. The two systems cross roughly at right angles.

men can safely stand and run in the upright posture. So strikingly do these structures show the direction of stress that when the famous engineer, Professor Culmann of Zurich happened (in the

[1] V. Markham. *Jour. Roy. Soc. of Arts*, 1950, **99**, 67.

year 1866) to visit an anatomist in his dissecting room, and saw the bony trabeculæ, he is said to have remarked with wonder that the bone was precisely similar to the crane he had just invented.[1]

Until a few decades ago, engineers and designers were unable to make use of many materials of great strength on account of a difficulty which is of a rather fundamental nature. In any uniform material, minute imperfection such as cracks are bound to occur. When a structure made of such a material is loaded, the stresses accumulate around an imperfection from which a process of complete breakdown spreads rapidly. (This is the principle used in tearing cloth or paper—a small cut in the right place starts a large tear.)

In nature the difficulty is solved by the use of fibres which are bonded together. Thus, in wood, cellulose fibres of great strength run along the grain but these fibres are bonded at right angles by means of the comparatively weak lignin. In recent years the method has been copied by industry. Thus cellulose fibres and glass are now bonded with resins. The great strength of glass fibre has thus become available for the construction of car bodies and the hulls of boats. In plywood, veneers of wood, with the grain arranged alternatively, at right angles, are bonded together. Precisely the same principle is used, for example, in the shell of the tortoise and in seed-containing pods. Similarly, the molecules out of which cotton is formed are arranged rather like the strands in a wire rope—spiralling in opposite directions.[2]

A few years back the Russians invented a "mechanical mole" for tunnel making.[3] It is said to work by faithfully copying the mole's technique of compressing earth at the back, so hardening the sides of the tunnel and reducing the need for much excavation.

Numerous other engineering devices and principles find their counterparts in nature. The close resemblance between the heart which pumps blood round the body and the pump of the engineer was realized in the early days of science. It was William Harvey who, seeing that both the heart and the tubes through which the blood passed were fitted with valves, reflected, as Boyle tells us, "that so provident a Cause as Nature had not so placed many valves

[1] See D'Arcy W. Thomson, *On Growth and Form*, 1942, pp. 973 ff.

[2] See R. D. Preston, *The Molecular Architecture of Plant Cell Walls*, 1952.

[3] *New S cientist*, December 13, 1956, p. 20.

without design," and it was this consideration which led him to the discovery of the circulation of the blood.

The methods of building up struts for bridges and aeroplane wings find an exact parallel in the arrangement of the bones in the eagle's wing. The principle of the ball mill—in which substances are ground to powder between moving steel balls—was employed in the stomachs of certain animals long before man was upon earth. For some animals deliberately swallow stones which are then used in the stomach for grinding food until it becomes digestible.

PAPER

Turning to technology, we all realize that the invention of paper is one of the most important—perhaps, indeed, *the* most important —invention that has ever been made. Yet here again man owes a debt to nature.

Until the end of the eighteenth century, paper in Europe had been manufactured from rags, but the French naturalist René Réaumur (1683–1757) noted that wasps used minute filaments of wood fibre to make their nests and that these were made of a material which was remarkably like paper. In a memoir presented to the Royal Academy of France in 1719 he declared that wasps "teach us that paper can be made from the fibres of plants without the use of rags and linen, and seem to invite us to try whether we cannot make fine and good paper from the use of certain woods". His suggestion fell on deaf ears but he emphasized the point again later in his great *Histoire des insectes* (6 vols.: 1737–48). While Réaumur did not himself make paper, the hint that he had thrown out was not forgotten and when, at the end of the century, the scarcity of rags became acute (shiploads of ancient Egyptian mummies were sent to America where the linen in which they were bound was removed and pulped!), methods of making paper from wood were developed. Later, in his six-volume work on paper-making, Jacob Schaffer again called the wasp the first papermaker and he actually re-made some paper out of pulped wasps' nests.[1]

WORLD WAR II

In World War II, numerous technical devices and methods were quite deliberately copied from the methods used by nature. Indeed,

[1] See Dard Hunter, *Papermaking*, 2nd ed. 1947, pp. 313 ff.

the Services employed biologists for the sole purpose of guiding research into finding the best ways of making the various appliances that were needed.

Thus, it was often necessary to land goods by air. The old method had been to attach them to a parachute but this had the disadvantage that they were liable to be blown away by the wind. Winged seeds, such as those of the sycamore and maple, seemed to point to an answer. In the end, the *sky-hook*, designed for loads up to a hundred pounds, was produced. It would reach the ground almost directly under the point of release, even in moderate wind. "But," writes Lord Brabazon modestly, "so far nothing comparable with the efficiency of the sycamore seed has been evolved . . . in this auto-gyro single-winged sycamore seed we have an example of a rotary movement combined with advanced aeronautics."[1]

The study of camouflage naturally assumed enormous importance and the methods which came to be used were largely developed under the guidance of biologists. The principles of *imitation* (mimicry in insects), *disruption* (as in the zebra) and *counter-shading* came into general use and were applied with great skill. As an instance of the last named, aeroplanes engaged on anti-submarine patrol, were painted white below—thus resembling such fish-eating birds as gulls, terns and gannets. For it was realized that a submarine about to be attacked by an aircraft is placed in much the same strategic position as a fish about to be attacked by a bird and the undercoating of white makes it difficult to distinguish the outline against the bright sky.

To turn to another story, it was soon recognized that the principle employed in radar, for the detection of aeroplanes at a distance, has a remarkable counterpart in nature. For the bat emits a series of high-frequency sound pulses, the echoes of which it is able to pick up. From the time interval that elapses before the echo returns, the bat can estimate the distance of the various objects in its vicinity and can apparently form a mental picture of its surroundings. So effective is this mechanism that bats can fly blindfolded between a series of wires which cross and re-cross a room. Certain fishes (notably *Gymnarchus niloticus*) which live in muddy water likewise emit and pick up electric signals and so have no need of eyes.

Another interesting principle is that of modulation—the broadcasts from wireless stations use a very high frequency carrier wave modulated by sound frequencies. But once more it transpires that the principle is not new—grasshoppers communicate with one another by means of a sound carrier wave of 8,000 cycles per second, modulated by a low frequency of less than 300 cycles.

CHEMISTRY

Chemistry already owes much to nature. Chemists have often wondered how it is that complicated chemicals which have taken research workers years of labour to build up in minute quantities are yet made in plants and animals with relatively little difficulty and in great quantities. In some instances (e.g. the synthesis of tropinone, artificial rubber, etc.) biology has shown chemists how to carry out elegant new syntheses in the laboratory, in ways which would hardly have been thought of otherwise.

But chemistry is concerned with an invisible world of atoms and nature's ways of doing things on the microscopic scale are far more difficult to discern than on the macroscopic—it was inevitable at first, that man should learn more from nature's engineering than from her chemistry, the secrets of which are still largely unravelled.

Yet the chemical methods of nature are, in general, far more efficient than those which are used in factories. No one doubts that the elaborate machinery used to separate oxygen from air—by fractional distillation of liquid air—is grossly inefficient compared with the quiet efficient way that nature uses. Perhaps the day will come when man will learn how to copy her—when we shall be able to use a cheap portable apparatus employing a circulating blood-like fluid, which will dissolve the oxygen from the air and liberate it once more when the pressure has been slightly reduced.

Again, if and when man can understand the workings of enzymes and can learn how to make these extraordinary substances for his own use, a new vista of civilization will be opened. The synthetic enzyme will be one of the greatest discoveries of all time and will at once enable almost any kind of organic material to be made economically from almost any other.

Another secret, of which as yet, we understand very little, is that of lubrication. In normal health, joints are never stiff—the ankle moves flexibly despite a load of 70 kilos. An engineer is contented if he can reduce the coefficient of friction between his moving surfaces to 0·1—even the new self-lubricating plastic PTFE gives a value of ·05. Yet in the joints of animals the value is not above ·01. The lubricating (sinovial) fluid is no better than man's lubricants applied on ordinary surfaces, but on the living bone the wonder is accomplished. There is a secret here that may one day revolutionize engineering. Similarly the ship designer is fascinated by the dolphin's ability to "lubricate" the surface of its body far more efficiently than man can, as yet, "lubricate" the hulls of ships and submarines.

Another wide field in which nature has pointed the direction is pharmacology. Since early days mankind has obtained most of his useful drugs from plants. The ideas that inspired many of the types of synthetic drugs in use today have had an origin in nature. Aspirin and the salicylates are a well known example and everyone is familiar with the enormous success which has attended the use of the antibiotics in recent years.

PHYSICAL INSTRUMENTS

From the earliest years of science the development of physical instruments has owed much to the existence of corresponding devices in nature.

The lens would seem to be a direct copy of the eye but the invention is lost in mists of antiquity—lenses were well known to the ancient Romans. At first lenses suffered from many kinds of aberration—one of the most serious being that the light of various colours did not all come to a focus at the same spot. Newton came to the conclusion that this defect was inherent in lenses and was theoretically insuperable. Yet, rather over a century ago, it was the realization that the human eye is corrected for chromatic aberration which showed that the problem *could* be solved, and which led to the development of the achromatic lens.

Our sense organs still enshrine many possibilities. The eye is still far superior to the best of modern cameras—it is much more sensitive than the fastest film, sees over a wide angle, presents a moving picture, and has the remarkable property that it remains effective despite enormous changes in the intensity of illumination, adjusting to such changes automatically. Another remarkable sense organ is the nose. It will detect stray molecules of at least fifty thousand different chemical compounds, often identifying them accurately. An instrument which would work on the same lines, if such could be made, would certainly be invaluable.

To turn to more recent history, the achievement of television may owe much to the realization that it is actually accomplished in our own bodies—the continually moving images of a moving panorama are transmitted through the optic nerves to the back of the brain where they are interpreted as sight. Again, the sensitizers used in modern infra-red photography have their counterpart in the pigments in the eye which appear, in part at least, to perform the same function.

One of the most important navigational instruments of the post-war era is the *gyrotron*. It does the work of a gyroscope but contains vibrating instead of rotating parts. The invention arose out of a close study of the small organs, called *halteres*, of the common fly which give it a sense of direction in space.[1]

DESIGN IN NATURE

So much for the facts. But what is their meaning? It is surely this—that man's intellect at its zenith, as often as not, manages only to discover principles which have already been in use for long ages, having been apparently invented long before ever man came upon the scene. If, then, we are entitled to speak of design when we refer to the works of men, it would appear to be the merest pedantry only which would restrain us from employing the same word when we think of the wonderful contrivances which, in nature, are so abundant. As well might we give the credit for inventions to those who plagiarize the work of others but not to original inventors themselves.

In short, the existence of design in nature is a fact which must certainly be taken seriously.

More and more, to-day, we turn to nature in order to discover the problems that are capable of solution. And again and again we discover that nature has provided a model which gives us more than a hint as to how our problems can be solved.

Often, of course, men have made inventions and have only later realized that the same methods were employed in nature. Yet the existence of the devices in nature has equally often been the spur to new advances and new discoveries.

[1] *Nature*, 1954, **173**, 572.

CHAPTER XII

DESIGN ARGUMENT—IN HISTORY

THE task which lies immediately ahead of us is to examine the implications of the conclusion to which we have been driven by a survey of modern scientific knowledge—the conclusion that design in nature is real and cannot legitimately be explained away.

But before doing so it will be necessary to tackle a wider problem. It is often claimed—and claimed rightly—that a religion or philosophy based upon an up-to-the-minute knowledge of science is of little value. Science, it is said, is an activity of man and its assured conclusions change from age to age. Theologians extolled the might and majesty of the God who had made the Newtonian Universe: they little dreamed of the Einstein who was to demolish the proud edifice. Half a century ago, determinism in the physical world seemed the most certain of all the conclusions to which man's mind had led him—yet today physicists are saying that they can find no certain evidence that the behaviour of the ultimate particles of nature is rigidly determined by their past histories.

In short, science is an inconstant and unreliable guide in the spheres of philosophy and religion. If the hearts of the faithful rejoice when they hear that astronomers have confirmed the Biblical statement that the heavens shall wax old as doth a garment, or the prophecy that the elements shall melt with fervent heat: if they sink at the news that a new ape-like ancestor of modern man has been unearthed—well, it only shows that their faith rests, not upon God and His word, but upon the ephemeral science of today; that is all. For the truths of philosophy and religion are eternal truths —they are not to be proved one day and disproved the next by chance changes in the winds of scientific opinion. Science in short, is irrelevant to the deeper issues of life. Let the scientists go their way, seeking truth where they can find it. But let them keep to their own fields of inquiry and realize that any conclusions they may draw can never directly impinge upon the fundamentals of religious faith. In this way only will it be seen that true philosophy and true science can never be at variance.

Such is a common point of view. And it is obvious that, if it be correct, we need proceed no further with our present inquiry. Having established the fact that there is design in the physical universe—and that design is as useful and as "real", shall we say, as force, mass, or distance—we must leave the matter at that. For, if we venture to proceed further, it is certain that we shall find ourselves sooner or later encroaching on the territory of the philosopher, the moralist and the theologian.

Now the only ground of the objection we have stated is this— that scientific conclusions are for ever changing with the intellectual climate of the day. And in so far as this is true, we may agree with those who object to an unwarranted use of science—it would certainly be wrong to use a very recent and debatable theory about the origin of radio waves in stars in order to prove, let us say, some particular proposition about the nature of the Trinity.

The issue confronting us amounts, then, to this. We have seen that the reality of design in nature is becoming increasingly apparent in modern science. But in stating this conclusion, are we merely giving vent to a passing intellectual opinion—a theory that might arise today and be forgotten a few centuries or even a few decades hence—or is our conclusion likely to be one of an altogether more permanent character?

To answer this question we must turn to history. We must inquire how the theory that the universe is designed has fared during the long centuries of changing science.

EARLY VIEWS

In many periods of the world's history science was virtually non-existent—science, that is to say, in the form of a co-ordinated mass of knowledge based upon man's observation of the world around him. Yet in all times and in all places men have observed nature and have wondered as to its purpose. In this sense, at least, science is perennial and, as we shall see, the contemplation of nature has exerted a profound effect upon human thought since the dawn of history.

In one form or another, the idea that the world was designed by a God or gods for the benefit of man is to be found in most of the primitive mythologies. Among the Hebrews we find constant expressions of this idea, as in the Book of Genesis, where God is said to have created first the world, and then man, whom He made ruler of created things. Much of Christ's teaching in the New Testament ("consider the lilies," etc.) is along the same lines, while later still we find Paul saying that the creation is a manifest proof of the eternal power and Godhead of its Creator (Romans 1: 20). Preaching to Gentiles, Paul and Barnabas declared that, although God had hitherto allowed the nations to live very much as they liked, the rains from heaven and the fruitful seasons were proof enough of God's interest in man (Acts 14: 17).

Similar, if less refined, ideas were common enough in the Pagan world of ancient times. Aristotle was profoundly convinced that the world had been intelligently planned—even down to details. His over-confidence in his reasoning powers makes us smile today. He asked, for instance, why it was that the dogfish did not have a mouth in front of its body like other fish, but one that was placed a little way down the flattened ventral surface of its body. After due reflection he concluded that this ferocious fish had been so designed by Providence to order to allow "a fair chance of escape to the smaller fishes." "Indeed," he gravely adds, "if it were not so, there would be very few of the little fishes left."

Belief in Providence formed a central part of the teaching of the Stoics. Cicero, in his book *On the Nature of the Gods,* makes Balbus declare that it would be as sensible to suppose that the world had come into existence by chance and without design, as it would be to "believe that, if a great quantity of the twenty-one letters, composed either of gold or any other matter, were thrown upon the ground, they would fall into such order as legibly to form the Annals of Ennius." Epictetus likewise compares the world to a house or a city and points out that just as these creations of man soon fall into disorder unless they are properly governed and taken care of, so the world, too, must have a Governor, without which it also would quickly become chaotic.

Pliny the younger, like Cicero and Aristotle, was greatly impressed by evidences of design in nature. The instances of design which he cites, sometimes seem quaint to us, but they were none the less seriously intended. "It is through her kindness," says Pliny, "that nature has provided man with an abundant choice of poisons so that he may painlessly destroy himself if, for one reason or another, he tires of life. Nature has also provided him with iron out of which he may make weapons of war"!

For Pliny, in fact, nature was a kind goddess who could do no wrong. Evil only came into the world when man started to interfere with the wise provisions of nature. Cucumbers, for instance, had recently been cultivated in Pliny's time and they were so successful and so prodigious in size that they quite monopolized the market—contrary, of course, to nature's intentions. What the ultimate outcome of this folly would be, the wise philosopher shuddered to think—he could envisage a day when the newly-created cucumber industry would fail: when, all too late, the peasants would discover that they had permitted nature's little delicacies to become extinct for want of proper care!

MIDDLE AGES

The early Christian apologists were emphatic in their belief that the universe has been made by God and that any unprejudiced mind, observing nature, could learn at least something about the Deity without the necessity for revelation. In the early Middle Ages, however, the influence of Neo-Platonism turned men's minds away from the study of nature and it was not until the time of the rediscovery of the classical writers and the influence of St. Thomas Aquinas (twelfth century) that attention was again directed towards nature as a source of knowledge about God.[1] However, even before the time of Aquinas, it is likely that most of those Christians who escaped the influence of the Neo-Platonists, continued to see evidences of God in nature. Thus Galen, the great Roman anatomist of the second century, whose work on the human body was the main source of anatomical knowledge throughout nearly a millennium and a half, had sought to show that every detail of every animal was designed for a definite purpose.

The fact that, in the Middle Ages, the reality of design was recognized in fields other than anatomy is well shown by the attention given to the subject by Job of Edessa (Baghdad, early ninth century) who sought to summarize all the known knowledge of science extant in his day.

"God," says Job, "acted wisely in making mountains for the help of mankind, and in making them high so that their waters

[1] See E. T. Whittaker, *Space and Spirit*, 1946

might flow." The clouds, too, had been placed high in the sky in order that rain might fall in drops. Job found further evidence of design in the fact that some metals were rare and some common, thus giving mankind a standard of valuation. In addition, he says, "The Creator made iron hard . . . so that it might cut and cleave objects, and be useful for the performance of crafts. Indeed, without it no craft can be performed."[1]

After the revival of classical learning, numerous writers in the West began to use the same line of argument. Thus, in the twelfth century, the Englishman Alexander Neckam argued once again that minerals had been made for man's benefit. But he saw an especial mark of Providence in the fact that nature had hidden most of the dangerous iron in the depths of the earth, where it was well out of the way of quarrelsome men. Had he but known of the vast stores of iron in the centre of the earth, the existence of which has been revealed by modern seismology, he would have considered his thesis vindicated beyond his wildest dreams.

Roger Bacon also, in common with his contemporaries, saw in nature the handiwork of God.

Later Albert of Saxony (fourteenth century) was one of the first to realize how remarkably the world must have been designed in order that land should rise up out of the sea. He developed the idea that a body has two centres—a centre of volume and a centre of gravity—and that these do not coincide in the earth. As a result one side of the earth is nearer to the sky than the other so that the waters are compelled to leave it bare, while the side which is farther from the sky is covered by water. This dissymmetry of the earth, he concludes, must have been designed by God for the benefit of animals and men.[2]

So profoundly were the Christians of the later Middle Ages convinced of design in nature, that they imagined that animals and insects had been made by the Creator chiefly to teach moral lessons to men. This motive lay behind the writing of the medieval *bestiaries* and, if it did nothing else, it certainly kept alive an interest in natural history—though only too often the writers of these quaint productions copied from one another instead of observing nature for themselves. (The attitude of medieval theologians towards natural history must have been strange indeed,

---

[1] *Job of Edessa's Book of Treasures.* Trans. A. Mingana, pp. 179, 183, etc.

[2] Pierre Duhem, *Etudes sur Leonard de Vinci*, Tom. 1, p. 18 ff.

for we read that, on one occasion, Stephen Langton [twelfth to thirteenth century], a former Archbishop of Canterbury, delivered a lecture in which he developed the theme that the red blood of a cow prefigured the blood of the Passion. At the close of his discourse he was confronted by a critically minded student who said: "It would be all the same if the cow had been black; the allegory is worthless. Whatever the colour of the cow, some sort of allegory could be found for it." Stephen was non-plussed. But later he quoted the words of the young man as an illustration of a horrid impiety that needed no refutation!).[1]

MODERN ERA

The Reformation brought with it a renewed interest in the subject of design in nature.

The early Puritans unanimously accepted the design argument.[2] To quote Preston, a representative Puritan writer of the period: "The purpose revealed in the creatures is, of course, that they serve man. Sun and moon and stars quicken the earth to bring forth plants to feed the beasts, and horses run, oxen plow, and dogs hunt on our behalf, so that we may consummate nature's work by serving God."

The first beginnings of modern science in the seventeenth century did nothing to produce a set-back to these views. Rather the reverse. Indeed, science was in large measure initiated by the belief that nature was God's handiwork. Nearly all the seventeenth-century scientists argued that, since nature had been made by God for man's benefit, man on his part had an obligation to try to understand what God had done for him. They believed, therefore, that man could serve God in no better way than by searching out the marvels of His creation. And conversely they believed that a lack of interest in science was a positively *sinful* state of mind—for it revealed a heartless indifference and ingratitude to the Creator who had so lovingly bestowed His gifts upon His creatures.

Early developments in science did much to strengthen belief in the wisdom and power of God. With the coming of the telescope and the microscope the wonders of creation known to man increased beyond his wildest dreams. The recognition of natural law showed,

B. Smalley, *The Study of the Bible in the Middle Ages*, 1941, p. 217.

See William Haller, *The Rise of Puritanism*, 1570–1643; 1938, p. 171. The quotation is given on p. 9.

yet more forcefully than before, that God had made laws for the proper governing of His world.

The early scientific movement reached its zenith in the work of Newton who shared the current views concerning design in nature. "This most beautiful system of the sun, planets and comets," wrote Newton in the second edition of the *Principia,* "could only proceed from the Counsel and dominion of an intelligent and Powerful Being. And if the fixed stars are the centres of other like systems . . . lest the systems of the fixed stars should, by their gravity, fall on each other mutually, He hath placed those systems at immense distance from one another."

In the eighteenth century the cause of natural theology suffered a certain set-back, especially on the continent. Yet, with the dawning of the nineteenth century, it was apparently more firmly established than ever. The earlier part of the century saw the best scientists of the day, under the ægis of the Royal Society of London, at work on the famous Bridgewater treatises, each of which was intended in its own sphere to extol and magnify the Creator of the marvellous designs to be found in God's "Book of Nature".

At this period one of the best-known books of the day was Paley's *Natural Theology*—a book which had extremely wide influence. Paley, well versed in all the scientific knowledge of his time, commenced by considering the stars and ended with the realm of living things. Everywhere, throughout the universe, he saw the evidences of design and though, at times, his enthusiasms led him to make somewhat fanciful conjectures (as in his treatment of the sloth, designed to walk slowly in order "to counteract the effects of repletion"—lest this animal's excessive greed should damage its digestive organs!), yet much of what he wrote remains true for all time.

Paley faced the problem presented by maladjustment and evil in nature with characteristic enthusiasm. For him, despite all that might be said to the contrary, nature was a sphere of almost unadulterated joy.

"It is a happy world after all. The air, the earth, the water, teem with delighted existence. In a spring noon, or a summer evening, on whichever side I turn my eyes, myriads of happy beings crowd upon my view. . . . A *bee* among the flowers in spring is one of the most cheerful objects that can be looked upon. Its life appears to be all enjoyment; so busy and so pleased. . . . The *whole-winged* insect tribe, it is probable, are equally intent upon their proper enjoyments. . . . Plants are covered with *aphides,* greedily sucking their juices, and constantly, as it should seem, in the act of sucking. It cannot be doubted that this is a state of gratification. What else should fix them so close to the operation and so long? . . . If we look to what the *waters* produce, shoals of the fry of fish frequent the margins of rivers, of lakes, and of the sea itself. These are so happy that they know not what to do with themselves. . . ." Paley continues by describing a crowd of shrimps in the sea which were about to leap out of the water together, after which he continues : "If any motion of a mute animal could express delight it was this : if they had meant to make signs of their happiness, they could not have done it more intelligently. Suppose then, what I have no doubt of, each individual of this number to be in a state of positive enjoyment; what a sum, collectively, of gratification and pleasure have we here before our view ! "

Nature, says Paley, may contain maladjustments, but there is little which gives the appearance of an intent to do harm. Fangs, perhaps, are in this category—yet even they are designed to kill suddenly and mercifully, not to cause unnecessary pain.

TURN OF THE TIDE

In the middle of the nineteenth century a reaction was staged against these views—a reaction which gained greatly in impetus by the fact that orthodox apologists "did protest too much."

In earlier centuries religious mystics had improved upon the doctrines of Providence to a scarcely believable extent. One of them went as far as to say that "bugs are serviceable for waking us up in the morning: mice teach us to be careful where we put things". The same doctrine of Providence was probably responsible for the old view that lice were intended to protect men from disease —a view held so ardently that even comparatively civilized people have often encouraged a symbiotic union with these troublesome little creatures!

As science developed, biologists who placed a religious interpretation on nature often allowed their belief to blind them to facts which did not readily fit in with their theory.

Naturalists continuously looked for design and harmony in nature and shut their eyes to everything which seemed to point in the opposite direction. They hailed with enthusiasm every discovery which seemed to suggest that "God had implanted a portion of his endless love" (Goethe) in the creatures and rejoiced at the discovery of monogamy in tortoises and of mother love in goats (Needham). But they had little or nothing to say about hook-worms and human deformity.

The subsequent reaction—led by Darwin, Huxley, Haeckel and others—was all the more extreme because the rapidly developing sciences brought to light many new facts about nature that had not been known before. The wonderful adaptation of the tapeworm to its strange environment, the remarkable life history of the malarial plasmodium, the detailed study of many newly discovered diseases, all seemed to point to a "design" in nature that was anything but beneficent. The newly rising school of biology tended increasingly to take the view that design in animals was an appearance only, to be explained by the theory of natural selection.

With this the beautiful picture of nature drawn by Paley and his contemporaries faded away. Naturalists vied with one another in a search for disharmony, ugliness, parasitism, useless organs and needless suffering. Romanes described the natural order of things in the now famous words: "We find teeth and talons whetted for slaughter, hooks and suckers moulded for torment—everywhere a reign of terror, hunger, sickness, with oozing blood and quivering limbs, with gasping breath and eyes of innocence that dimly close in deaths of cruel torture."

The same attitude infected even the physical sciences of the day. Whereas an older generation had imagined that the universe had been created, that matter had been formed from nothing by the word of God, that natural laws were the expression of God's will for His creation, that the physical earth showed evidences on every hand of the judgement of God against evil men, the upholders of the newer evolutionary philosophy sought to do without God altogether. Matter was now proclaimed to be eternal and self-subsisting: its properties were such that universes, suns and planets would necessarily come into existence of their own accord: physical law became the expression of blind unintelligent necessity, no longer did it require a Creator or Law-giver. As for the physical earth, the old Wernerian hypothesis of catastrophe was given up and replaced by the much more philosophically pleasing notion of uniformitarianism. Even in astronomy, where it had at one time been held by all astronomers that the heavens showed no sign of chaos or disorder, a newer generation declared that the heavens were chiefly in a state of disorder but that it was a principle of blind mechanics that disorder should spontaneously produce a certain amount of order if left to itself. Again, the earth had at one time been regarded as an exceedingly important object in the universe, an object specially prepared by God for man, His most wonderful creation. But now, as the telescopes peered farther and farther into the heavens, the earth became more and more lost in insignificance.

It was not in science alone that the new attitude revealed itself. Indeed, it had developed far in other realms of thought long before the days of Darwin. Malthus in his *Essay on the Principle of Population,* published first in 1798 had introduced it into economic theory. He had argued that all human society was doomed to a continuous war of extermination between the strong and the weak. Mankind could reproduce his species faster than he could make food materials available and, therefore, he was destined to live on the border of starvation or die in a struggle for existence.

In literature the same despairing pessimism had early begun to reveal itself. In a fascinating book Praz[1] has told the story of how the love of untarnished beauty seemed to disappear in the minds of literary men at the end of the eighteenth century and became replaced by "the tempestuous loveliness of terror". Poets gloried in tainted beauty, in hideous imaginations of death, in Medusas, in the beauty of Satan, and in the extremes of sadism. And soon the glories of the sunset, the insects and the flowers were to become mixed with the thought of the talons, the hooks and the suckers.

Thus the new view of nature, introduced first of all by the Romantics, spreading slowly through every domain of human thought until it became firmly entrenched within the precincts of science itself, finally undermined the old design argument for religion. A newer generation declared that the universe contained no evidence of design whatever, save only in living things. But in this sphere they refused to take appearances seriously, partly because, as they said, many natural organs were seemingly designed for evil ends and, partly, because the current science of the day proclaimed that appearance of design could now be explained away. Nature had merely selected those individuals upon which chance had bestowed her fortune, while the rest, an innumerable

[1] M. Praz, *The Romantic Agony,* 1933.

host, had perished miserably by the way. Nature was as full of the appearance of design as Paley had said, but it was an appearance only: biology had no need of the hypothesis of a Designer.

Today we are learning that this picture of nature is false, that the earlier scientists were right after all.[1] And it is significant that, even in the hey-day of Darwinian science, many of the arguments of the earlier naturalists remained unrefuted—and forgotten.

The geophysical features of the earth and the properties of water and carbon dioxide were not less wonderful because, ostrich-like, Spencer and Haeckel refused to consider them seriously. And as for the attempt to explain away order in biology—even Darwin himself was never convinced that he had explained it *all* away. No wonder that multitudes of simple people continued to use the argument from design and to ignore what the professors chose to say about it—and they were right.

This short survey of the history of our subject shows, as clearly as any survey could show, that the recognition of design in nature is no ephemeral scientific conclusion based upon the researches of a decade or two in the history of science—a conclusion which might at any time be reversed were a few new facts to come to light. Rather it is a conclusion which has stood the test of thousands of years: a conclusion so certain that if it should one day transpire that it is a gigantic mistake, man would have every ground for doubting whether valid conclusions of any kind can be reached by thinking.

So, finally, we return to consider the criticism with which we started this chapter. If it be true that it is dangerous to found philosophical and theological conclusions upon the changing science of the day, it is nevertheless desirable to distinguish between scientific conclusions which are ephemeral and those which are likely to prove enduring. And the existence of design in nature must be placed in the second category.

What conclusions then, if any, may we draw from the existence of design in nature?

[1] See especially F. Wood Jones, *Design and Purpose,* 1942; L. R. Wheeler, *The Harmony of Nature,* 1948, and R. E. D. Clark, *Darwin– Before and After,* 1948, 1958.

CHAPTER XIII

MIND IN NATURE——?

AT the present time it is probable that a large majority of those best qualified to judge—scientists and philosophers—are in agreement with the conclusion which we have now reached: the conclusion that design is one of the most striking features of the universe.

But ordinary men and women will not be satisfied with this. People in all ages have, as we have now seen, found in nature a proof of the existence of a God who was responsible for the underlying design. How does this argument stand today? Can we still argue from design to a Designer?

It is sometimes assumed that the answer to this question must be a firm negative and in this chapter we shall consider the chief objections which are raised today, against what is called *natural theology.*

ORDER OR DESIGN?

In the first place, it ought to be mentioned that, although there is much agreement as to the facts, there are many who insist on describing them in such a way that no implication of natural theology shall emerge. Thus Lawrence Henderson speaks of the *order* rather than the design of nature, because, as he candidly admits, he does not wish to use a word that might imply the existence of a Creator. And, following his example, the use of the word *order,* to cover the facts which we have been considering in this book, has become quite widespread.

The difference is partly one of words. Nevertheless, it is important to note that, if the word *design* is objectionable because it implies a designer, it is also true that the word *order* is apt to give a totally wrong impression about the fact that it is intended to describe.

For order is of two kinds. The man who paints a picture, orders paint upon canvas, but when a pile of sand is placed on a tray and shaken vigorously, the sand orders itself to form a layer, equally thick all over the tray. By the first kind of order we mean design and the implication that it implies an orderer in no less and no more than the implication that design implies a designer. The second kind of order, however, arises from the working out of the ordinary laws of nature and, in the light of physical science, we know that, although it may sometimes appear to the eye as if new order has arisen in the process (as when a crystal grows) yet, taken as a whole, order always tends to be lost.

Thus the word *order* is ambiguous and its use may lead us to overlook a very real distinction. The examples of design which we have considered in this book all represent order of the first kind— they arose in defiance of the ordinary laws of nature—they really *did* result in the formation of more order than could have been there to start with (no one can reasonably doubt that this was so, for instance, in the creation of the universe).

It is no accident, therefore, that those who speak vaguely of the "order of nature" also generally fail in the end to distinguish between what the theologian would call the *natural* and the *super-natural*. Such people start by using one word to cover two totally different conceptions, and finish by denying that science gives any warrant for making a distinction which they themselves have obscured. Dr. E. W. Barnes and Canon C. E. Raven, neither of them ignorant of science, afford two good illustrations of theologians who seem to have been led astray in this manner. Everywhere in their writings, they are emphatic that the creative power of God is at work in nature but, in a highly quixotic way, they lump together, for example, the creation of the universe itself, where order arose from disorder or even from nothing, with the more trivial physical events of the laboratory in which order disappears.

Since this confusion of thought has largely arisen as a result of the ambiguity inherent in the word *order*, we have in this book preferred the use of the older term *design*.

ON BEING VAGUE

So much for the facts and for the language in which we may seek to describe them. But can we go further? And should we even if we can?

Many agnostics urge that we should leave the matter at this point. We can never know, they say, what the cause of design may be or even whether it has a cause. It is better, then, that we should regard design as an unfathomable mystery—like causality or force —something in which we must believe because we find its evidences in nature, but about which we can usefully ask no questions at all.

Among agnostics who argue in this way are those who, like Lawrence Henderson, believe that it is almost dangerous to attempt to penetrate further into nature's mysteries: [1]

> It seems to me clearly established in the history of thought that when this problem (that of order in nature) arises the only safety is to be found in retreat and in employing the vaguest possible term which can be imagined, from which all implication of design or purpose has been completely eliminated. By common consent that term has come to be recognized as *teleology*.

However, it seems clear that Henderson's attitude was determined not by impartial consideration, but by his pronounced theophobia. For him "the only safety" means, apparently, the only safe way of avoiding a theistic conclusion. He never seriously attempts to discover whether such a conclusion is justified. His appeal to the history of thought is beside the mark—if former generations failed to develop clear ideas on a subject, that is no reason why we should not do better today. Still less is it helpful to retreat behind the high-sounding word "teleology"—hoping thus to forget the existence of ends or purposes in nature by translating the conception into Greek! As well might we refuse further to consider the origin of the light of fireflies when once it had entered our heads to say that the insects were luminescent.

SCIENCE AND TRUTH

It is at this point that the positivist will enter the field. He claims that ultimate reality is always unknown to us and that it is our business to stick rigidly to the facts we know and on no account to be dragged into postulating things that cannot be known or detected. Even mind, he will tell us, is a meaningless entity for we can never detect or measure it. We should therefore confine our attention to

[1] *The Order of Nature*, p. 204.

such facts as that the universe exhibits design or that man behaves in certain ways, and leave matters at that.

The positivist will remind us that this procedure—this refusal to postulate unobservables—has had considerable success in physics in recent years. Questions about the properties of the medium through which light waves travel have ended in futility, as have also attempts to measure absolute motion. Relativity is the attempt to connect together phenomena which we observe and so avoid asking useless questions about things that cannot be detected in any conceivable way. The modern scientist, we are told, is not really attempting to discover truth at all: he is merely correlating his sense data.

The claim that science has abandoned the pursuit of truth is often made, sometimes with astonishing dogmatism, but it is difficult to say how far it should be taken seriously. While we admit that there are certain things in the universe which at present transcend man's understanding, especially in connexion with the ultimate particles and processes of nature, yet it certainly is not true that science as a whole has abandoned the search for truth. Kekulé's discovery that benzene contains a closed ring of six carbon atoms, Harvey's discovery that the blood is circulated by the heart, the discovery that insects find their way by smell, that some grass-hoppers have hearing organs on their legs, or that the atoms in a crystal of salt are arranged in a certain pattern are discoveries that are true for all time. The aim of science is still to discover absolute, not merely relative, truth, about the world of nature. It is only a small group of physicists, whose outlook seems quite unusually narrow and specialized, who have ever seriously denied this and, even when they have done so, they have never attempted to show how biological and chemical knowledge can be brought into their scheme of things.

It is true that in a few fundamental though very specialized branches of physics—especially in the study of atoms, space, etc.—difficulties of interpretation are so formidable that, as a temporary measure, physicists have had to abandon the search for truth and confine themselves to making sense of measurements. But every physicist knows that, were someone to discover a way in which this difficulty could be overcome, the physicist himself would be the first to welcome the return to a search for truth.

The idea that modern physics is unconcerned with truth about nature, though it finds advocates among some scientists, is by no means generally accepted. A less extreme view was that of Einstein who believed that, although the laws (i.e. mathematical formulations) of physics are man-made, yet the physicist is exploring the ultimate structure of a real world when he discovers protons, electrons, etc.

As for the claim that the scientist is concerned only with the things which his own sense organs (aided by physical instruments) can detect, this also is untrue.

No one who is at all conversant with the history of science will be likely to question the fact that progress would never have been possible at all, were it not for the fact that scientists have freely postulated an invisible world behind the scenes.

INVISIBLE WORLD

Organic chemistry, for example, made headway in the nineteenth century, because chemists boldly imagined atoms that were arranging themselves in various ways, much as if they were balls held together by wires. At that time no one ever hoped to see or detect an atom. Opinion was, in fact, emphatic that atoms were so small that it would never become possible to detect them. Thus it was often argued that since the diameter of atoms is much smaller than the wave-length of light, no possible refinements in the microscope could ever enable man to see them. (At that time, electrons and X-rays were undreamed of, so that electron and X-ray microscopes were beyond the mental horizon of the day.)

Many hundreds of other instances of the amazing advances which have come about because scientists have boldly imagined a world that lies behind what is visible and directly detectable in nature might readily be given, though to appreciate their significance technical knowledge of the sciences concerned is often necessary. The following are some further examples.

The atom, the movement of molecules as a result of heat and the self-diffusion of gases, the existence of neutrons, mesons, neutrinos, Radium D (by Rutherford), etc., in physics; unconscious memory, desires, thought, etc., in psychology; new planets, stars beyond the range of telescopes, a creation epoch of the universe, invisible stars in spectroscopic binaries, etc., in astronomy; germs, filter-passing viruses, genes, recessive characters, etc., in biology and genetics; the existence of the element fluorine (despite the failure to isolate it for seventy years), the existence of free radicals such as methyl and ammonium, and of the latent photographic image, etc., in chemistry.

Even Lucretius, for all his scepticism on matters theological, built his philosophy upon argument of the same kind. In order to explain the things he could see he was forced to make hypotheses about things he could not see. "Clothes hung up on a shore which waves break upon become moist, and then get dry if spread out in the sun," he writes, "yet it has not been seen in what way the moisture of water has sunk into them, nor again in what way this has been dispelled by heat. The moisture, therefore, is dispelled into small particles which the eyes are quite unable to see. . . . Nature therefore works by unseen bodies."

These and other examples show us that science is concerned with the discovery of truth and that it cannot proceed unless it is prepared, at times, to postulate what are often termed *unobservables*.[1]

Science, therefore, can give little support to the positivist: it affords no ground for the claim that we ought to be satisfied with the fact of design but that it is unnecessary to ask questions as to its cause. Such an attitude would soon prevent discovery in nearly every line of investigation.

Indeed, *positivists* have done much to hinder the progress of science. Auguste Comte, their founder in the nineteenth century, declared that it would never be possible to ascertain the nature of the matter out of which stars were made. He even denied the possibility of chemistry as we know it today: "The real mode of agglomeration of elementary particles is, and must ever be, unknown to us, and therefore no proper object of our study."[2] Even into the present century positivists attacked the atomic theory. But for all their insistence that this, that and the other view was theoretically unknowable, knowledge has advanced. We need to learn from their mistakes, not to repeat them.

---

[1] It is now fashionable to restrict this word to describe what can never be, *if present theories are right*, observed (e.g. motion through the ether), and to regard other unobservables (e.g. the back side of the moon in pre-Sputnik days) as potentially observable. But confusion is easy and the distinction, though useful in physics, is perhaps unimportant for philosophy.

[2] *Cours de philosophie positive*, Paris, 1930–42. Vol. III, p. 115.

DESIGN AND INSTINCT

A third point of view has been urged in recent years, especially by Laird,[1] who argues that design is by no means always the product of mind. The squirrel hides nuts for the winter, the spider knows how to build its web, with the oncoming of cold weather birds migrate to warmer climes—all of them actions which *seem* to be designed with various ends in view. And yet, by common consent, they are not really so. Animals do not sit down and think how they may solve the problems with which they find themselves confronted in nature. We do not know how they solve their problems and we hide our ignorance under the word *instinct*. But even though this word is a coverage for ignorance, the existence of instinct does show us that design is not necessarily the outcome of the thinking of some person. When, therefore, argues Laird, we find design in the world of nature, we are under no necessity to imagine that it was brought into being by a Designer.

Laird's difficulty is not as great as he supposes. There are two points to be considered. First of all, let us consider our own semi-automatic responses. We walk, cycle, drive, type, and even talk and write with little mental exertion. We do not have to think which way to turn the bicycle wheel when we are falling over—the impulse to move the handle-bars correctly arises spontaneously. We rarely give a thought to grammar when we talk. As with animals our behaviour *seems* designed, but it is not the immediate result of conscious thought.

What conclusion can we draw? That we ourselves are impersonal automata? That design arises in the absence of a designer? Of course not. Every one of the actions we have mentioned is the result of past thought. When first we cycle or walk we have to think very seriously about the way we operate our muscles and, when we try to talk in a foreign language, we know what it is to be acutely aware of the grammar we use. Sometimes, although we ourselves think little about our acts, the reason is that we are entering into a heritage left by the thoughts of others. We do not have to think how to turn on the electric light switch, but the design of switches required a great deal of conscious thinking a generation or two ago. Again, thinking is not always conscious. Discoverers and

[1] John Laird, *Theism and Cosmology*, 1940.

inventors tell us that brilliant ideas often come to them suddenly when their minds are at rest, occasionally, even, in dreams.

In everyday life, a sudden need to escape from danger may lead us to do the right thing before we have time to think about it—or at least to know that we are thinking about it. Every psychologist is familiar with the idea of the unconscious mind, where scheming and planning may go on about which the conscious mind knows nothing. The minds of many animals, perhaps also of young children (at all events in the embryonic stage) seem to be akin to our own unconscious minds. The sleep-walker can solve simple problems—can find his way out of bed and avoid obstacles. And E. S. Russell describes how caddis-fly larvæ, confronted by very simple problems with which neither they nor any other members of their race, could ever have been confronted before in their whole ancestral history, can yet solve the problems—each one in its own way.

Many biologists believe that instincts have arisen in this way.[1] A problem has been solved by an individual animal: others have copied it and, ultimately, it has become enshrined in the make-up of their progeny. In recent years a tom-tit discovered how to break open the metal seals of a milk bottle and the habit soon spread widely over the country. Similarly an individual pair of swallows must once have discovered the value of making their nests in the eaves of a house and the habit later became widespread.

Acquired habits are not passed on to the next generation. But the researches of C. H. Waddington have shown that *ability* to learn a new habit *is* inherited. After a very few generations a habit which formerly took a long time to learn, is mastered after a few tries. This is also a familiar fact of everyday life. A generation ago dogs were slow in learning to keep off motorized highways but today it is otherwise. Careful researches on the song of birds has shown that if a bird does not hear the song of other birds of its kind, it will not instinctively sing their song and, with patience, it can be made to learn the song of alien birds. But as soon as it hears the usual song of its species, it picks it up at once and forgets how to sing in the new-fangled way. The same principle of inheritance accounts for the fact that birds such as nightingales can sometimes build up a tradition of song in certain localities.

Although newly formed habits are not passed on directly to the

[1] For example, J. A. V. Butler, *Inside the Cell,* 1959, p. 135.

new generation it seems likely or at least possible that after many hundreds or thousands of generations the habits do in some way become genetically fixed. This seems the most natural explanation of the elaborate habits of bees, wasps and termites. Similarly the migrations of some birds make little sense today—as when mountain ranges have to be crossed with much resulting fatality—but they make sense if the habits were fixed in prehistoric days when the topography of the earth was different from what it is today.

It seems reasonable, then, to suppose that instinctive acts were usually in the first place the result of mind and were often consciously planned (no doubt the tom-tit *wanted* the milk inside the milk bottle on the doorstep). But of course accidents would have happened too. A fly might have laid its eggs in all sorts of places, but only those which were laid in the flesh of a certain caterpillar, which happened to be particularly nourishing for the grubs, eventually survived. After many generations the habit might become fixed. The outcome of such accidents would not, of course, be in all cases aesthetically satisfying. They may be thought of as results of a limited creative power possessed by natural selection.

It seems, then, that instincts give no ground for dissociating design from mind. In fact, we are faced by much the same problem when we ask about the origin of instinct as when we ask about the origin of bodily structure. Both, in general, show design. But we may find a few relatively simple cases in which chance followed by natural selection will account for the facts, just as we may find examples of modifications of bodily structure which could be accounted for in the same way. In fact, the appeal to instincts is irrelevant. We might just as well appeal to anatomy. Instincts are part of the argument for design—not necessarily design by an almighty Designer but often by an individual animal.

MATERIALISM

We turn now to a different class of objection. For the old-fashioned materialist, mind is something incapable of existing apart from matter. It is regarded as an *epiphenomenon* of the structure and metabolism of the brain—a well-worn analogy compares it with the *light* of a candle, an incidental side-show in the combustion of wax. Since, therefore, matter necessarily came before mind, the materialist maintains that it is misleading to suppose that nature can be mind-like.

This view is no longer defensible because it assumes, without evidence, that "matter" (we use the word, of course, to cover the subject-matter of science, i.e. everything which can be made to appeal to the senses, including, for example, energy and magnetic fields, etc.) is the only reality. To say that mind is an epiphenomenon of brain is to say that matter, in this case brain matter, is what we start with. But it is easy to prove that "matter" is not the only reality. Thus everyone agrees that prime numbers exist. They would still exist if all life in the universe was extinguished for if, in some future aeon, life appeared once more, a new race of men would again discover prime numbers. (This is what we usually mean by the word "exist"—a chair exists in a room when there is no one present because it would be found to be present, if someone came into the room.) Mind discovers prime numbers but it does not create them. Prime numbers therefore exist, but they are not material.

Again, recent work in the field of psychical research is hardly consistent with a materialistic picture of mind. There is now much evidence for believing that, in telepathy, ideas themselves, not codes of ideas enshrined in a material medium (e.g. as "dots" and "dashes" in Morse, as modulated electro-magnetic vibrations, or as deviations in the grooved track of a record), appear to be capable of travelling from one mind to another—they certainly travel and therefore must certainly exist where brain matter is absent.

Philosophical reasoning leads to the same conclusion. We know that there is a difference between truth and falsehood. If we say that a man has told a lie or has discovered a new law of nature, we are not *merely* making a symbolic statement about the movement of electrons in his head—to hold that view is to undermine the foundations of morality and of science alike. In addition, it is to undermine the materialistic position itself—for it is pointless to assert that mind is an epiphenomenon of brain if the statement means only that the electrons in the head of him who makes the statement are moving in a certain way: an opponent might rightly retort that the electrons in his head make the opposite view "true" for him and all discussion is then at an end.

It follows, then, that mind stands in a unique relation (though we do not understand precisely what this relation is) to things that are certainly outside the sphere of the exact sciences—to truth and also, probably, to goodness and beauty. And this being so, it would be strange indeed if mind, so obviously related to the non-material, should itself be material.

Added to this, there is the difficulty that, as we have seen, the ordinary concepts of physical science are, in the last resort, unintelligible except in terms of mind or of the experiences of mind. So far as the evidence goes, then, there is no more ground for saying that mind cannot exist in the absence of matter, than there is for saying that matter cannot exist in the absence of mind. Indeed, the latter view has more to commend it than the former.

It is pointless to argue against this conclusion that mind and matter cannot have completely separate existences, for otherwise they would not interact. For we should hardly expect to understand their interaction in any case. Prime numbers and brains are as different modes of being as we could well conceive, but somehow they *do* interact—the mathematician discovers the numbers and writes them on paper. Ultimately we know very little about the structure of the universe and pettifogging objections based upon our lack of understanding are not of the type that a scientist would raise but belong only to a world of unrealistic philosophy. If we wish to look for analogies, we may say that two worlds may be different but may yet possess a small zone where they occupy something in common.

Thus the chief difficulty which the materialistic Victorians felt about interpreting the universe in mental terms has largely disappeared.

But there are other ways, also, in which the progress of science has made the old materialism much less plausible than it was once thought to be. Science has made us increasingly familiar with instances in which organized matter enables a non-material and invisible reality to show its presence. The earliest example of this was afforded by magnetism—the element iron providing one of the few ways in which the otherwise undetectable magnetic field can be detected. But today we are familiar with numerous other examples of a like kind. We do not doubt that the space around us is humming with thousands of messages—with Morse, with music, with speech and with moving pictures—yet it is only when a very highly organized system of wires, condensers, resistances, thermionic valves, transistors, etc., is present, that we become aware of this astonishing fact. We know, too, that an exceedingly small technical fault in the apparatus we use will distort the messages we receive or perhaps altogether prevent us from perceiving them.

The analogy is not perfect, but it does acquaint us with the idea that highly organized matter may be necessary to make manifest an invisible entity at the back of reality which would otherwise be altogether beyond the range of our senses.

Now no one would dream of arguing that because a faulty contact in a wireless television set completely alters the appearance of the picture on the screen, that therefore the picture is a property of the highly organized matter out of which the set is made. And it would be equally absurd to suggest that, because the mind ceases to function properly in disease, or because the behaviour of a man is altered when he takes a small quantity of a dangerous drug, that therefore his mind is a property of his highly organized brain-matter. Obviously such facts are only what we must always expect with highly organized systems: they throw no light whatever upon the nature of mind.

Thus the development of science is making it increasingly clear that the traditional arguments used in support of the materialist view of mind are all of a kind that are totally irrelevant to the point at issue. Any one of them might be used with equal effect to disprove the need for a directing intelligence in a car or locomotive. "Poisons" in the fuel (e.g. a trace of free bromine in petrol), mechanical faults, inadequate oxygen or excess of carbon dioxide in the air, lack of water or "vitamins" (e.g. lubricants containing, as in high pressure oils, minute but essential traces of complex sulphur compounds), may one and all result in the breakdown of a machine, just as their counterparts may cause a breakdown in the machinery of the body, preventing the mind from exercising control over behaviour.

Thus, an increasing mass of knowledge with which we are becoming familiar today—no more than the fringe of the subject can be touched upon here—is most easily explained if we suppose that it requires the very highly organized and specialized matter which we find in the brain in order that mind may make its presence manifest. In the light of much modern research on the powers of the mind, and also of our increasing familiarity with highly organized systems, the old arguments against the dualist view are beginning to appear in an increasingly unfavourable light. Were it

not for widespread philosophical prejudice (see later, Chap.
XVII) it is probably fair to say that they would find few to sponsor
them today.

REGRESS

A fourth argument is of another kind. It is agreed that design
probably implies a designer, but we are told that it is useless to
argue in this way, for it gets us nowhere. It is often said, for
instance, that to suppose that God made the universe is simply to
push the difficulty back a stage without doing anything to solve it.
For if we say that the universe was made by God why should we
stop there? Why should we not proceed to ask who made God
and then who made the being who made God and so *ad infinitum*?
In short, since any attempt to answer fundamental questions about
the universe must involve us in an infinite regress, is it not better
to take nature as we find it without asking questions?

To this we may rightly retort that, if this advice were to be
carried out consistently, we should know nothing about the world
in which we live. All scientific explanations are liable to start an
endless train of questionings. If we say that salt is made of sodium
and chlorine ions, we may ask what they are made of. Of protons
and electrons. And they? We do not know, but even if we *did* the
sceptic might ask what that in turn was made of and so *ad infinitum*.

In the same way, we may ask what holds the world in space. We
may decide it is the sun's gravitation. And what holds the sun?
Again, the question is unending. So far as ultimate answers are
concerned, science has not yet put us in a better position than the
Hindu who said that the earth rested on the back of a tortoise and
the tortoise on the back of an elephant, but was nonplussed when he
was asked what the elephant was standing on.

Such objections can be raised against all scientific theories. Yet
we do not hear it argued that matter does not consist of atoms
or that the earth is not held in her orbit by gravitation, simply
because these assertions might tempt an awkward child to ask an
endless string of questions. In fact, this particular objection is
rarely or never heard except in the form "Who made God?" The
fact that sceptics use it so often here but never think of using it in
connexion with all the other beliefs they hold, surely suggests that
they are not looking for truth at all but are simply looking round

desperately for some plausible way of escape from the inevitable conclusion to which their reason leads them.

Again, the question "Who made God?" implies that mind needs making. If we ask who made an aeroplane, a car or a railway we are satisfied when we learn that a person or group of persons was responsible—we do not think of asking who in turn made them. For mind is itself creative and we have no reason to suppose that it needs making in the same way that other things do.

MAN'S CREATIONS AND GOD'S

A fifth objection to the view that nature was created is as follows. It is suggested that there is no real and close analogy between creation by man and creation by God. Creation by God might mean creation out of nothing—that God uttered His voice and the whole universe came into being. Such an event is quite outside our experience. But creation also involves the idea that formless matter was created and/or arranged in a certain way—and here there is a plausible analogy between what man does and what God is supposed to have done at the beginning of time. Just as the artist, the sculptor, the chemist or the writer mould materials at their disposal —be they paint, stone, molecules or ink—so it is supposed that God used the matter out of which the universe was made in order to realize His plans.

Now it is just here, so we are told, that the analogy breaks down. For man can only mould his materials because his brain can actuate his hands and fingers with which, alone, he orders matter, whereas God has neither brains, hands nor fingers.

The analogy is, however, much closer than may at first sight appear. The fingers and hands are as it were the accidents, but the working of the mind certainly does afford a very close analogy to what we may suppose was done by God in creation. For, in order that our muscles shall function at all, it is essential that at some level in our brains, our minds should act upon matter, making it behave in an ordered way. All that we accomplish, all our highly ordered and purposeful activities, must have their counterparts in the brain at some level—even if it be at the level of the molecules themselves. Our minds do act directly upon matter and the material world is arranged according to the plan that was pre-

viously conceived by mind. From this conclusion it would appear
that there can be no escape.

Other considerations make the analogy even closer. Poltergeist
phenomena are most easily interpreted as due to the direct action of
mind upon matter. Although many are not unnaturally sceptical as
to their reality, it is difficult to resist the mass of evidence on this
subject that is now available.

There are many facts of medicine which suggest a similar view.[1]
How else can we account for the enormous influence of mental
disposition upon the body? Thoughts suggested in hypnosis can
lead to the rapid healing of wounds. Those who are determined to
do so can often die as a result of sheer will power; those who are
full of faith may recover from very serious diseases. It is difficult
to avoid the view that in instances such as these we see a direct
action of mind on matter in a way that does not correspond to the
normal physiological functioning of the body. And if mind can act
upon matter in our own experience, it seems reasonable to suppose
that events of a like kind, though of course on a vastly greater scale,
might once have happened in nature.

Thus the analogy between what we know of our own minds, and
what we must assume about the mind of a Creator who made the
universe is, perhaps, as close as it could be. But, even if it were
much less close than it is, it would scarcely be fair to raise the point
as an objection. In that event, the critic would only be saying that
man's mind is not an *exact* working model of his Creator's. But why
should it be? Today, many scientists are prepared to concede that
man can hardly hope to imagine working models of ultimate reality.
There seems little point, then, in demanding a working model of
the great Designer which represents Him so accurately that at no
point does the analogy fail.

QUESTIONS

Yet another argument, the sixth, which became popular between
the wars, arose out of the philosophy of the late R. G. Collingwood.
According to Collingwood, people in each age tend to ask questions that are peculiar to their time. Rationalists who have absorbed
his teachings often argue that the quest for God in science arises
only because certain people are in the habit of asking the question:

[1] See Helen F. Dunbar, *Emotions and Bodily Changes*, 4th. ed., 1954.

"What kind of a Force or Power brought the universe into existence?" Now this, they say, is as unanswerable as: "What is the ultimate nature of space?" or "What is the colour of an electron?" We know that such questions cannot be answered and we should not, therefore, persist in asking them.

Now it is true that at certain periods in history men are more interested in some questions than in others, but this does not mean that all questions must be discounted. There is no more reason, on the surface, for asserting that the question: "What kind of a Force brought the universe into existence?" is unanswerable, than there is for saying that the question: "How do bats find their way in the dark?" is unanswerable. To find out if questions are unanswerable, we must be prepared to ask them and to look for answers—any other attitude is a manifestation of prejudice. Beyond this, perhaps, little needs to be said.

CONCLUSION

We have examined several common arguments for the view that design in nature cannot lead us to believe in the existence of a Designer at the back of nature. There are others—some of which have been alluded to in earlier parts of this book, while we shall consider yet others later on—but few if any of them are even so much as plausible. After studying the subject, it is difficult to avoid an overwhelming conviction that all these arguments are little other than attempts to evade the obvious. That this is so is confirmed by the fact that, although there is such widespread agreement that the existence of cosmic design should not be probed, there is no agreement whatever as to why this should not be done—some offering one excuse and some another.

Those who seek to argue that science can tell us nothing of God, seem often to be curiously unaware of the nature of explanation. Reality can, as already observed, be understood only in terms of ideas that mean something to our minds. Contrary to popular opinion, even the revolution in physics has made no real difference to the situation. The fundamental ways in which we seek to understand the world remain the same today as ever they were. No matter whether we are discussing a star, an atom or the universe at large, we still think in terms of energy, time, mass and distance—

all of them concepts which, as we have already had occasion to observe, are anthropomorphic in nature.

Relativity does not teach us that mass and time are meaningless —it does teach us of relations between mass and energy and, some would add, between time and space. All our understanding is couched in anthropomorphic terms and we can have no reasonable cause to object if facts almost compel us to invoke the most anthropomorphic of all of them—that of a mind-like quality itself. Indeed, such an explanation may be as near to absolute truth as mortal mind can approximate.

To this conclusion many moderns strongly object—a reaction, no doubt, from the over-elaborated metaphysical theology of days gone by. But the new attitude is as far removed from reason as the old. The modern refusal to deduce God from science reminds one, indeed, of a man who, rather than make unwarranted inferences, informs the police that he was robbed one night of his purse and watch by *lonesomeness* and *darkness* instead of by an unseen criminal.[1] Common sense will never be reconciled to the view that design is to be dissociated from the conception of a mind-like power which brought it into being.

Those who argue against belief in a Creator often fail to realize that most of their arguments might be turned against science itself. Some complain that we cannot see God but can only infer that He exists, but forget that the same objection applies to thousands of scientific facts which all men everywhere accept. Others say that since we cannot tell *how* God created the world there is no point in saying that He did so, but the same people are often warm supporters of the theory of evolution which they accept uncritically as a fact, though they do not know how variations—the raw materials of evolution—occur. Some, again, appeal to the mere use of language, as if the whole matter could be settled by an appeal to definitions. We are told that God, if there is a God, must, by definition, be all-powerful, or all-wise or all-something-else. They proceed to point out that since there is evil in the world, God cannot be both all-powerful and all-wise or that, since we have freedom of choice, He cannot be all-knowing. Therefore, they say, there cannot be a God. But they conveniently overlook the fact that by proceeding in this purely verbal manner it is possible to disprove not the existence of God only but of atoms also. Leibnitz, the great

[1] B. J. Duffy, *Food for Thought*, 1944, p. 146.

philosopher of the seventeenth century, argued in the following way. By definition, he said, atoms are small infinitely hard bodies. But since they are infinitely hard, it follows that they cannot rebound when they strike one another, for if they rebound it must be because they suffer deformation. Since by definition, they cannot suffer deformation, it follows that if there are atoms they would not rebound and the whole universe would suddenly become quiescent—all movement would cease. Therefore, since movement continues, there can be no atoms.

And so we might go on. It is probably no exaggeration to say that there is not a single argument against belief in God—including the argument from the existence of evil (see later, Chap. XVI), which could not, with equal ease, be used to disprove the existence both of atoms and also of many other established facts of science.

CHAPTER XIV

DESIGN AND ITS CRITICS

IN the course of this book we have discovered that in one respect
at least, there is an almost mind-like quality about the universe.
In every main branch of science—physics, geophysics,
astronomy, chemistry, biology—we are faced by the same surprising
fact. Nature is not constructed in conformity with the laws that we
discover in the laboratory but seems rather to have been brought
into existence in opposition to those laws. Nearly everywhere it
shows the signs of apparent planning: of something that we can
only think of in terms of ingenuity and deliberate design.

SCIENTIFIC ANIMISM

What is the meaning of these facts? While acknowledging their
existence, many moderns are exceedingly unwilling to accept them
at their face value. Remarks made upon the subject, sometimes by
well-known scientists, seem often intended merely to divert attention from the problem by their wit and extravagant use of analogy
rather than to access the situation fairly. What other interpretation,
for instance, can we place upon the following words which are
typical of much modern writing? "Nature is far ahead of us in her
methods and in her achievements. But it must be remembered that
she has had an enormous start." Here the simile suggests that
nature and man may be likened to two teams of research workers,
one of which, possessed of an unfair start, was able to solve many
difficult problems while its rival was still floundering in the dark.
The analogy is so bold and pleasing that we are apt to overlook its
implication—the implication that nature, like man, can think,
invent and design: that she is endowed with primitive animistic
qualities. And though it is explicitly denied that in reality nature
is quasi-personal, yet the habit of spelling her with a capital N
belies the denial.

Thus, in order to account for the existence of plan and design in the universe, the materialist is often compelled to use animistic language. Does he do so simply to avoid belief in a personal Deity behind nature? It is difficult to find an alternative explanation.

ANTHROPOMORPHISM[1]

But the materialist is ready with his defence. It is essential for scientific thought, so he will tell us, that anthropomorphic ideas should not be introduced. For they are a mere throw-back to the views of the Middle Ages and they must necessarily hinder advance in science. Thus, in the old days, chemical reactions were attributed to the love or hate of substances for one another: those which reacted quickly did so because they were more alive or "quick" ("*quick lime*," etc.) than others, and so on. Likewise, in astronomy, the celestial spheres were pushed round by angels, a Prime Mover manipulating the outermost sphere, while the paths of the heavenly bodies were supposed to be perfect because they were circular. Matter celestial and matter terrestrial were also supposed to differ from one another in that one was perfect and the other imperfect.

In biology, we are reminded that the same tendencies showed themselves to an even more marked degree. Paracelsus postulated a quasi-human cook who lived in the stomach and prepared the meals which reached him through the œsophagus. Diligence, ingenuity, mother love, fear, happiness and so on were ascribed even to insects. Psychologists "explained" abilities by inventing faculties. Thus a boy who sang well was supposed to do so because he had an innate singing faculty, no one noticing that all such "explanations" were tautologous.[2] In the same way opium was said to induce sleep on account of its dormative propensities.

So we are reminded that the scientist of today has rebelled, all along the line, against purely anthropomorphic explanations of the world around him. It is not that he objects to them in principle so much as that he realizes that, unless we resolutely refuse to advance hypotheses of the kind that cannot be tested by experiment, scientific advance is impossible. We may suppose, if we like, that

[1] The dictionary definition of this word is "conception of God under the form of a man". We use it here in a wider sense to cover all attempts to understand the exterior world, including God, in man-like terms.

[2] Materialists who despise the old faculty psychology conveniently forget that, in their own scheme of things, the universe evolves, produces life, mind, etc., because it has the latent power or faculty of being able to do so.

apples fall to the ground because they have an innate tendency to do so, or that spiders build webs in order to exercise their ingenuity. It may be so—but such hypotheses are the dead end of knowledge. To advance them is merely to baptize with a name the very phenomena that need to be explained, whilst doing nothing to clarify them.

Historically scientific progress was only possible when, at last, all anthropomorphic explanations were set aside and theories and hypotheses were confined to those the truth or otherwise of which could be tested by a direct appeal to the results of experiment.

For this reason, so it is asserted, it would be both wrong and unscientific to take the apparent design in nature at its face value. No conceivable experiment can enable us to determine whether or not the chemical atoms were intended to fulfil a purpose, the energy of the universe "wound up" or the structures of animals designed. To assert such things is to assert the unprovable; to think in a way grossly at variance with the established canons of scientific thought. Moreover, far from explaining the fact that seems so mystifying, the design hypothesis baptizes it with a name and leaves it as inexplicable as ever.

SCIENTIFIC EXPLANATION

For this attitude we may at first feel some sympathy. Yet, on examination, it turns out to be based upon assumptions so false, and upon thinking so careless, that it is difficult to suppose that anyone would take it seriously, were it not that a certain small group of rationalist writers repeat the story so often and with an air of such finality that—well, many people have come to imagine that the case for the abolition of anthropomorphic ideas is incontrovertible!

Firstly, then, as to the nature of scientific explanation. It is evident that, if we are to explain the universe at all, we must do so in terms that mean something within our experience.[1]

Colour means nothing to the man born blind, nor sound to the man born deaf. Now scientific explanations, like explanations of all other kinds, depend in the last resort upon an analogy which we imagine to exist between the world outside and the world within: the world of nature and the private world of experience. Natural forces would have no meaning to us were we unfamiliar with forces

[1] Jeans, *Physics and Philosophy*, 1942.

within our own experience—the pushes and pulls which we feel in our muscles. Time and distance would be inconceivable but for the fact that we find them intimately woven into the pattern of our minds. If philosophers are to be trusted, even the concepts of natural law and of cause producing effect would be meaningless were it not that we are familiar with the fact that our own volitions cause our muscles to operate. Energy would be incomprehensible if we did not experience its activity in everyday life. Or again, a person completely ignorant of mathematics can have no conception of what physicists mean when they interpret phenomena in terms, say, of the Schrödinger equation—physicists only understand what they themselves are talking about because they imagine that nature is like something, namely mathematical equations, with which their own minds are already familiar.

In short, *all* explanations are in the last resort anthropomorphic. Force, inertia, causality, time, space and mathematical laws are no more and no less anthropomorphic than love, instinct, hate and design.

To this it might be retorted that the theories of physics are always of a kind that admit of test by observation, whereas no one can test the existence of instinct or design. Yet even this plausible statement is not true. Consider, for example, a simple hypothesis. It seems extremely likely that the property of inertia which bodies possess is dependent, in some way, upon the existence of the fixed stars—that if we could accelerate a mass of a pound on a planet that was completely isolated in space, it would no longer have a mass of a pound. (Thus Mach pointed out that, relatively speaking, there can be no difference between swinging a stone round on the end of a piece of string and holding the stone and string still while the whole universe is rotated round them. This suggests that centrifugal force, and so acceleration and inertia in general, is not a property of matter as such, but only of matter in a universe.)

Now this hypothesis cannot be tested by experiment for we can never bring our laboratory beyond the confines of the universe! Yet it is a physical hypothesis none-the-less and has often been taken quite seriously by physicists.[1]

Again, the hypothesis that evolution took place in the early ages

[1] D. W. Sciama, *The Unity of the Universe*, 1959. About 80 per cent of the inertial mass of bodies is believed to be due to regions of the universe beyond the reach of the largest telescopes.

of the world cannot be tested by experiment but it is often dog-
matically asserted to be true. Similarly, astronomers have devoted
much attention to the birth of nebulae, planets, etc., but their
theories cannot be tested.

As Born and others have pointed out, many of the concepts of
physics are untestable. No one can devise an experiment to
determine whether causality is or is not true. The use of equations,
such as the famous Shrödinger wave equation, assumes that space
is continuous—but no experiment can verify this assumption. Many
other examples might also be given.

From this discussion two points emerge. First of all that, other
things being equal, a theory which can be tested by experiment is
certainly to be preferred to one that cannot. But where other things
are not equal or where it is impossible to suggest a testable theory,
scientists have rarely hesitated to suggest one that cannot be tested.
And, secondly, that although it is sometimes true that physical
theories are more readily tested than so-called anthropomorphic
ones, this by no means always follows. To say, therefore, that
science has overthrown anthropomorphic explanations and has
replaced them by impersonal ones is to give a totally false picture
of what has, in fact, taken place.

We see, therefore, that it is unconvincing to argue that, because
design is undetectable, science will be hindered if we conclude
that nature is designed. Such a conclusion would be quite wrong.
A person who is studying the mechanism of a medieval clock is in
no way hindered in his work if he recognizes that the clock was
designed for a specific purpose—namely to show the time. Science
is concerned with partial causes and, even if we assume that these
partial causes are always mechanical, it is irrational to jump to the
conclusion that the universe as a whole is undesigned when
evidences of its design are staring us in the face.

Far from hindering progress, the recognition of purpose and
design in nature has been generally helpful rather than otherwise
in scientific research. In the early days of the scientific era it led to
such discoveries as the circulation of the blood (see p. 147), Kepler's
laws and the principle of least action (Maupertuis). Today, the
intuition that bodily structures or chemical compounds are present
in organisms for a purpose, that they are fulfilling a role in animal
or plant economy, often stimulates research into what that purpose

may be. (Research workers have more than once expressed this sentiment to the writer.)

The last argument—the argument that by using the word "design" we merely baptize or name a problem without otherwise shedding light upon it, we shall consider at a later stage.

HUME'S ARGUMENT

Yet a third line of reply to the design hypothesis is the argument of the philosopher Hume—the argument that since we should not exist at all if things were other than they are, all evidence of design is illusory.

We have already (p. 32) had occasion to refer to one form of this argument—the hypothesis that the universe "winds" itself up every now and again by chance and that, rare as they are, such freaks are bound to happen occasionally in the long run.

In our earlier discussion we saw that the argument is baseless and that it undermines all scientific knowledge. However, if rigidly adhered to, it is of course unanswerable. In no matter what form it is used it does, however, place the one who holds it outside the realm of reason. For a materialist, who refuses to accept the reality of design in the universe on the ground that it is a stagnant idea which cannot be tested by appeal to experiment or observation, to put forward in its place the notion that apparent design has no significance, is little short of incredible. How does he know that it has no significance? How does he know that we are alive only because things are as they are, or that we are living in an epoch shortly after an era of "rewinding" of the universe? What experiments or observations can he point to in support of this claim? And, if it be true, how can the hypothesis lead to advance in knowledge? Is not the idea at least as stagnant as that of design?

To these questions surely there can be no answer. Every argument that can be used against the design theory can be used with equally telling effect upon the hypothesis of Hume. And since the design theory is supported by so great a wealth of fact whereas that of Hume rests only on unsupported conjecture—what is there other than prejudice which should induce us to take the latter seriously?[1]

---

[1] It may be added that, say, books on electronics could not exist unless the art of printing, etc., already existed. But this is no argument that such books (or the art of printing, etc.) can arise without design.

UNITY OF NATURE

We have examined the reasons commonly advanced by those who refuse to take the apparent design in the universe at its face value and have found them wanting. But what positive reasons can we advance on the other side?

First of all, it is a canon of reason that we ought whenever possible, to accept the most natural and straightforward interpretation of the facts with which we are confronted. This alone creates a strong presumption in favour of the reality of design in nature— for all agree that design is *apparent*.

Secondly, the general course of scientific development over the last century or so has provided us with good ground for thinking that this conclusion is correct. Many developments have shown a wonderful inter-relatedness among phenomena. Things which, to bygone generations seemed wholly unrelated, have repeatedly turned out to be connected in a very intimate way. Who, for instance, before the nineteenth century would have imagined that electric charges could be related to magnetism or that the osmotic pressure of solutions could be related to their freezing-points? With the coming of relativity theory and of modern physics, many more unifications have been effected.

Now these advances in physical science have been concerned with mass, temperature, distance, time and other quantities which can be weighed or measured. It is the fact that they are measurable which makes it possible to represent them (or rather the numbers that measure them) mathematically.

Now we have no grounds for supposing that reality is confined to what we are fortunate enough to be able to measure. Unifications that have been discovered, both in physics and biology, certainly suggest that the unity of nature is something wider and broader than that so far discovered.

Why should we be surprised, then, to discover that wholly distinct branches of science have this in common, that one and all show evidences of a plan or design which runs, as a unifying principle, throughout the whole domain of nature? The recognition of this design is not a quasi-scientific irrelevancy, introduced by philosophers, or theologians; it is the climax of a unifying tendency within science itself.

Science has, to a large extent, shown us how to make sense of the universe, but the recognition of underlying design in facts that have never and probably will never be brought into relation with materialistic scientific thought, brings us to a climax in our intellectual understanding of the world in which we live. It gives us a vision of a unity far more striking than any of the unities within limited fields which we learn about in textbooks of science. Those who talk lightly of this amazing fact, speaking of it as if the idea of design were only a throw-back to medieval thought, or the hiding of facts by a mere word, show only that they have never given the matter the attention that it merits.

HISTORICAL PERSPECTIVE

Thirdly, the discovery of design in nature must also be seen in historical perspective. In the nineteenth century it was often taken for granted that science had "got to the bottom" of nature. It was tacitly assumed that future progress would consist, chiefly, in filling in details or making measurements with increased accuracy. But the subsequent history of science has belied these expectations.

Modern discoveries have chiefly impressed upon us the limitations of our knowledge. The fundamental secrets concerning the nature of electricity and of matter, of the functioning of the cell and of the brain, of the origins of the universe and of life are all hidden from our view. New discoveries made in ever-quickening tempo, undermine all the confidence that was expressed within living memory. The old belief that chance can explain the universe becomes more and more unlikely as the years pass—for the universe is bigger and the complexities of nature are altogether more surprising than anyone had anticipated. The trend of research is not towards explaining more and more of the fundamentals of nature in terms of chance and mechanism, but the exact reverse. It is the evidences of cosmic design, not of chance, that are accumulating. To say, therefore, that in postulating "design" we put the clock of science back, is sadly to misjudge the developments of our day. It is science itself which is showing that the old materialistic notions, though they have their place when we are studying isolated parts of nature, can never give us a satisfactory picture of the whole.

SPECIALIZATION: ITS RESULT

Finally, we may ask why it is that in some circles—though probably in a diminishing number—the existence of design in nature still fails to receive recognition.

Probably the cause is to be found in the scientific specialization of the present time, more than in any other single factor. Only too often scientists are profoundly ignorant of the work of their colleagues in an adjacent laboratory—physicists often know nothing of plant physiology, meteorologists nothing of genetics or organic chemistry, zoologists nothing of thermodynamics. In these circumstances a scientific worker, faced in his own field with an apparent instance of design, naturally regards it as isolated and exceptional and proceeds to explain it away with as much ingenuity as he can muster.

As far as the author is aware, all writers on the subject who in the past have reached the conclusion that the universe is undesigned, have treated design in this piecemeal fashion. Eddington, who, though admitting the cogency of the argument for creation based on entropy, was disposed to reject it on (as Russell points out) grounds that were chiefly emotional, ignored the evidence from chemistry and largely ignored that from biology. Many lesser writers have followed his example, often seeking to explain away —by fallacious arguments to which Eddington would never have descended—the arguments for design that physics affords.

Others, however, following the lead of Darwin, have attempted to explain away the apparent design of biology while conveniently ignoring that afforded by physics, astronomy and chemistry. This is the line adopted by J. S. Huxley and by a number of those who, like him, have attempted to devise a "religion" based on evolutionary science. Sherrington, Wellbye, Gordon, Alexander[1] and, for the greater part, the Marxists, have adopted this procedure. It is possible to read their books in vain for the least realization that the order which they so nonchalantly explain away in biology, by the principle of natural selection, has any affinity with the design

---

[1] J. S. Huxley, *Religion without Revelation*, 1927; R. F. D. Wellbye, *What the Future Demands of Religion*, 1942; R. G. Gordon, *The Philosophy of a Scientist*, 1948; J. Alexander, *Life, its Nature and Origin*, 1948, etc. For a Christian attempt along these lines, written by a Jesuit Father, see Teilhard de Chardin, *The Phenomenon of Man*, 1960.

that is found in other spheres of science. Sometimes, indeed, they condescend to mention entropy, only to dismiss it in a paragraph or two—rarely more—of head-shaking agnosticism. For the rest, the structures of plants and animals are, for them, the only examples of apparent design in the entire universe and so, of course, they must be explained away—generally by evolution, though even evolution is often unconsciously exalted into a quasi-magical, quasi-personal force which invents things, seeks to make higher values emerge and even designs offspring to fit them for the struggle of life. We have already seen how the wonderful inventiveness of nature has been dismissed by the claim that, after all, nature (personified as a team of research workers) had a many-million-year start of man.

Sometimes, indeed, such writers are not merely departmental in their attitude, but seem to confine their interests to a department within a department. Even biology is not considered as a whole and most of the evidence discussed in Chapter X is conveniently ignored. Instead, it is implied that tse-tse flies and tape-worms represent 50 per cent of the instances of design that nature can provide and, in the philosophies that are spun, these organisms are allowed to loom inordinately large.

Turning to chemistry, we find far fewer attempts to explain the facts away but a greater tendency to ignore them altogether. Yet even here, the subject is sometimes treated departmentally. Tyndall, for example, is commended for his argument that, if we suppose that the expansion of water on freezing is designed, we must suppose that the expansion of solidifying bismuth is designed also. Again—the evasion would be reasonable enough if, on investigation, the apparent design of a *single one* of the properties of water turned out to be a highly exceptional phenomenon in nature. But when we find numerous unexpected properties, all apparently purposeful, it is misplaced ingenuity to explain them all away.

Again, there is the mathematical argument—the argument that since much of nature can only be made intelligible in terms of mathematical equations which are developed by the human intellect, it must also follow that the designer of the whole of nature understands mathematics—that he is a pure mathematician, to use the somewhat ill-advised language of Jeans.

Here again, attempts have been made to argue that nature is not in reality mathematical at all, but that the mathematics is introduced by man who must not be surprised if, like the conjuror, the rabbits which he secreted in his hat emerge for all to see.

Now this view, though it may perhaps express a half-truth, can hardly represent the whole story—for theoretical mathematics has, especially in recent years, led to many striking physical discoveries. Yet once again, it appears as if those who regard the evidence for design which mathematics affords, in isolation from all other evidence of design, are naturally disposed to explain it away as best they can. But when once we cease to see it in isolation, the need for these evasions disappears.

The numerous attempts that are made to avoid belief in design are so very partial, their propounders so obviously labouring under the misapprehension that the one science with which they happen to be familiar is the only one that affords evidence of design, that it is difficult to take their conclusions at all seriously. With science as departmentalized as it is at present, it is surely no cause for wonder if some scientists profess that they can see no widespread evidence of design in nature. But the evidence is there as those who are prepared to study the sciences as a whole may readily discern. Indeed, the reality of design in nature is rapidly becoming recognized as one of the most important and far-reaching conclusions of modern science.

CHAPTER XV

COSMIC MIND

"It would therefore not only be extremely sad, but utterly vain, to attempt to diminish the authority of that proof. . . . We have nothing to say against the reasonableness and utility of this line of argument, but wish on the contrary, to commend and encourage it."

> Immanuel Kant on the argument from design
> ("physico-theological argument"). *Critique of Pure Reason*, Trans. Max Muller, p. 502.

IN the last chapter we have seen that there must be, at the back of nature, a Mind which, though vastly greater than our minds, must yet be purposive in the same sense as our minds are purposive.

But what further conclusions can we draw? Before asking this question we must anticipate a difficulty which many feel—though it is one that has concerned us in disguised forms already. There are those who will say that having spoken of Cosmic Mind, we should state clearly what we mean by the words. A definition must be given.

ABOUT DEFINITIONS

Now it is here that we find our way barred. A definition of Cosmic Mind is impossible. And no wonder. For we cannot even define what we mean by our own minds—let alone the minds of others. It would be foolish indeed to seek to define, precisely, what we mean by the distance between two stars while remaining blissfully ignorant of the meaning of the same word as applied, say, to the distance between our hands and our feet. In the same way we cannot expect to define the mind of God when we can neither understand nor define human mind. But that provides no more reason why we should disbelieve in the existence of the former than in that of the latter.

The demand for definition arises from two sources. Firstly, the desire to define each term precisely is a legacy from medieval philosophy. But secondly, although modern science gets on well with very few definitions, this fact is generally obscured by the modern textbook. Thus we may read that the mass of a body is "defined" as the ratio of the mass of the body to some standard mass—that of the standard kilogram or pound. Here, of course, the word "defined" is wrongly used—"measured" would have been more appropriate. For, having discovered that our body weighs twelve stone, we are still quite in the dark as to the nature of its mass. Such a definition is as irrelevant as it would be to propose to define the mind of a boy by measuring how much cleverer he was than some other boy. The fact is that physics, in common with many other sciences, gets on well in the absence of definitions but that the writers of textbooks are anxious to hide the fact in order, we may suppose, to confer an air of respectability upon their subjects.

As we have already noted, human understanding depends upon the ability to draw analogies between an exterior world and the experiences with which we are directly familiar. It is in this way and, perhaps, in this way alone that we can understand the meaning of Cosmic Mind.

IMPERSONAL FORCE

But to what kind of a Cosmic Mind does the evidence point? There are some who say that this Mind must be an impersonal Force, not to be endowed with any of the characteristics which we associate with our fellow men—that He must, in fact, be impersonal.

On this subject, perhaps, there has been more muddle-headed reasoning than in almost any other field of thought. Aldous Huxley argues (or at least implies) that God cannot be personal because those who used to think He was personal burned heretics at the stake. He implies that people who believe in a personal God will come to believe that their own enemies are God's enemies. Concerning this argument it is, perhaps, sufficient to say that the follies of men cannot change the eternal facts about the universe!

Again, Winwood Reade in the *Martyrdom of Man* confuses the issue by a mere play on language: "The supreme power is not a mind but something higher than a Mind; not a force but something higher than a Force; not a being, but something higher than a Being; something for which we have no words, something for which we have no ideas." The irrelevancy of such an observation will be obvious enough if we apply it in another connexion. What should we think of an astronomer who asserts that, since the magnitude of the heavens is so vastly greater than that of the earth, it is absurd to suppose that stars possess mass—that we must postulate instead something that is not mass but higher than mass: "something for which we have no words and no ideas"?

Others, such as F. W. Westaway, try to make out that belief in a personal God who is ultimately independent of nature is childish and immature. And the difficulty he resurrects is the old gibe of the Epicureans in Cicero's day: "How did God occupy Himself before He created the universe, and how did He come to fix upon the particular date of creation?" And so we are told that "this pathetically solitary pre-creation figure is a survival of primitive anthropomorphic picture-making. God is represented as a sort of much-magnified man rarified to mere mind, existing by Himself, with no sort of relation to anything else. How childish it all seems!"[1]

More prejudiced language it would be difficult to imagine. First of all it is assumed that because God can be represented as a survival of something which primitive people believed, the idea is unworthy of our attention. This is the old fallacy of judging the pudding by the cook's pedigree—with a vengeance. As well might one condemn chemistry on the ground that it is a survival of primitive alchemy. And as for the argument that there could not have been a God before He created the universe because, if there was, *homo sapiens* ought to know precisely how He spent His time in the pre-creation epoch—it can only be said that it is on a par with the philosophical argument that mind and matter cannot be distinct, because if they were it would be possible for man to imagine how they could interact! What we need most in all such discussions is a due sense of humility. As yet we do not know how a muscle works, how a plant grows, how our minds think or even why our brains need a plentiful supply of blood. Space, atoms and energy again leave us floundering in mathematical guess-work—totally unable to comprehend the things for which our symbols stand.

[1] *Obsessions and Convictions of the Human Intellect*, p. 382.

To suppose that on these ultimate issues our inability to understand a state of affairs has any relation to whether that state of affairs exists, shows a degree of conceit to which it would be hard, indeed, to find a parallel.

Others, again, assert that God is impersonal because in the company of trees, mountains or glaciers, they become acutely aware of a reality in nature that is not material. Such an experience is, of course, consistent with belief in a personal God and it is often so interpreted. But those who have been brought up to believe that God is impersonal or non-existent sometimes react by deifying— or all but deifying—nature. In this way an attempt is made to link together the new experience with an old way of thinking and the very vagueness with which such ideas are expressed, seems to show how ill all these wonderful and very real experiences of man accord with the materialistic conceptions of our day.

NO-THEORIES

Considered logically, of course, impersonal theories of God are what we may call no-theories. They purport to explain the facts we observe in nature—but they do nothing of the kind. We discover design and purpose and, in order to account for them, we invoke some Power of Force which, as far as we know, will in no way help us to understand how they arose. The expression "Impersonal Being" is, in fact, meaningless—no experience with which we are acquainted can give us even the faintest glimmering of understanding as to what that Being may be like. To speak of such a Being at all is to ignore all the recognized canons of thought. It is as if we spoke of an impersonal person, or an unforce-like force or an undistance-like distance—a mere meaningless contradiction in terms.

As C. S. Lewis has pointed out, the roots of the impersonal theory of God are more deep seated than any mere logical argument might lead one to suspect. The impersonal view has often appealed to those who have wished to retain the glamour and comfort of religion while at the same time dissociating themselves from the moral obligations which belief in a personal God entails. Particularly was this so among the leaders of the Third Reich—Rosenberg in *Der Mythus* and Hitler both in *Mein Kampf* and in many of his speeches, referred repeatedly to God, but both were violently prejudiced against any personal theory of His nature. It is not difficult for the most cultured Englishman to feel the attractiveness of the same doctrine—perhaps, indeed, most of us have been tempted by it at times.

Impersonal ideas of God enable man to make the best of both worlds—he can enjoy the ritual, the reputation or the comfort of religion and avoid the overwhelming conviction that his religion demands his life or that he is personally responsible to a God with whom he will one day have to reckon. The temptation to evade these considerations is not, surely, one which appeals only to the worst of men—it appeals to them strongly enough—but one that appeals to every man and woman no matter what his reputation may be. And if we find that it appeals strongly to us, it is all the more imperative that we should examine the credentials of the impersonal theory.

PERSONALITY IN GOD

Can we say then, that the Creator is personal? Not exactly. We must be careful not to use words which imply that God can be comprehended as a giant man—that imply that He is a person and nothing more than a person. That personality is at least a part of what He is we may be reasonably certain—but there may be vastly more about Him which we have not so much as begun to comprehend as yet.

In what way then is the Creator personal or, to put it more accurately, in what way is personality one of the attributes of the Creator? Let us consider the facts. In the first place, the Power that made the universe must have been intelligent for, on every hand, we see signs of His intelligence in nature. And since the universe was evidently planned with a view to the future, matter being prepared for the coming of life long before life arrived, we can hardly avoid the conclusion that the Power must have seen the end from the beginning: must have worked with very far distant ends in view.

If we are prepared to agree thus far, it is difficult to stop here. If the Power co-ordinated nature with a view to events that still lay in the future, He must, presumably, have had a *desire* to do so and He must certainly have known the meaning of what we call *motives*. Presumably, too, He must have known the meaning of *pleasure,* or at least of *satisfaction*, in His work. Of course we cannot be certain on these points—yet they seem to represent the most reasonable view that we can take. And if this be so, God must have known the meaning of many, at least, of the values that mean so much to us.

Now these are characteristics which we associate with personality. Indeed, we often judge personality by the ability to work for far-distant events. The baby, like the dog, seizes what it fancies and satisfies its desire at once, the university student gives up the immediate pleasures of country walks, of courting or of reading fiction for the sake of an examination that may lie months or even years ahead. It is in the self-discipline of working for far-off ends that personality matures. And it is in this respect, too, that we find personality in the Creator.

Thus, all the evidence we possess points overwhelmingly to personality in God. If we build theories which ignore this fact, we shall show our failure to appreciate evidence.

But how, we may ask, do we know that there is only one Person and not a whole multitude of persons?

Firstly, one Person is the simpler hypothesis, so we ought to adopt it unless we have reason to the contrary.

Secondly, the universe has the appearance of forming a co-ordinated whole. As far as we can judge the same physical laws hold in the farthest confines of space as those that hold on earth, while the study of spectra reveals a universe that is all made of one kind of matter. As Whittaker points out, this discovery of our own time would have delighted Aquinas in the twelfth century for, in the Middle Ages Aristotle's view that matter situated beyond the orbit of the moon differed essentially from terrestrial matter was generally accepted. Modern discovery, therefore, lends great plausibility to the view that there is but one Creator.

GOD'S NATURE

Hitherto we have often avoided the use of the word God. And that for a good reason. There are many who claim that natural theology, though it may tell us of the existence of a cosmic clock-maker possessed of enormous ingenuity and power, is irrelevant to religion because it can tell us nothing about the more vital problem of whether the Creator is or is not a moral Being.

This argument owes its persuasiveness, chiefly, to the existence of evil in the world. Leaving this point for consideration in the following chapter, there is one further criticism which ought to be mentioned before summarizing the conclusions we have reached so far.

The objection is one which is often raised by the religiously minded person. "True," he may say in effect, "science apparently leads to belief in a cosmic Creator. But such a limited conclusion is of little value—for science can never prove that God is *infinite* in His power, wisdom and goodness. And it is this knowledge for which religious consciousness seeks—nothing less will do."

This argument reveals a misunderstanding. We have only to contemplate the vastness of the universe, the immensity of the time scale in which the cosmic drama moves and, at the other extreme, the wealth of complexity revealed even in a drop of pond water, to feel our own littleness beside the Creator of these things. The purely theoretical difference between the infinite of the mathematician and a vastness so stupendous that we are dazzled when we try to comprehend it, is of little if any importance.

The concept of infinity is a modern one—no Hebrew or Greek word in the Bible denotes it. The Bible speaks of God not as *infinitely* mighty but as almighty—mightier than all: not as *infinitely* wise and good but as being Wisdom and Goodness. It is a strange religious consciousness indeed which, dazzled by the popular use of a fiction of mathematical theory, asserts that it can never rest satisfied with a conception that has satisfied the saints of all ages until comparatively recent years.[1]

In medieval theology God was said to be infinite. But the word had not the meaning that it possesses today. God was held to be infinite in the sense that in Him was to be found, to perfection, all possible attributes—attributes of love, goodness, knowledge, etc.

It seems fair, then, to conclude that science points unmistakably to the existence of a Creator of vast intelligence, of limitless power and wisdom, and yet personal in the fullest sense. It shows us, moreover, that the Creator is not a part of nature, but beyond nature and therefore supernatural—since by working intelligently upon nature He causes *super*natural events to take place contrary to

[1] F. R. Tennant, *Philosophical Theology*, Vol. II, p. 264, traces the incursion of the mathematical notion into theology. Even in mathematics "infinity" probably has no literal meaning—See P. W. Bridgman, *The Way Things Are*, 1959.

physical laws. There are many, it is true, who take exception to the word *supernatural*. It is true that if, by nature, we mean everything that exists, whether material or spiritual, the word has no meaning. But this is to misuse language. In nature we observe regularity and law but nature itself also provides overwhelming evidence that, in the past, nature's laws have sometimes been reversed, that a power from without has intruded. The word *supernatural* appropriately describes this fact.

Such is the direction in which our reasoning has led us. But can we trust our reason? There are many who have been brought to this point but who yet, on seeing the evil in the world, have turned back convinced that there is an irreconcilable inconsistency in the universe—an inconsistency which man can face in only one way— the way of agnosticism. To a consideration of the existence of evil we must therefore turn without further delay.

CHAPTER XVI

EVIL

"I, that have examined the parts of a man and know upon what tender filiments that Fabrick hangs, do wonder that we are not always sick."

Sir Thomas Browne, *Religio Medici*

THE evidence we have marshalled provides overwhelming justification for belief in a Mind behind nature. But as yet we have said little about moral values. The facts with which we have been concerned hitherto are mostly consistent with belief in an immensely clever demiurge—a being capable, indeed, of arranging atoms in intricate ways but quite unconcerned with goodness, truth, or the deep aspirations of suffering man; a God who is a scientific hypothesis, but not the God of religion.

Such is the argument that is often used today—and pressed home so strongly that many, even among the most religious of men, now profess themselves wholly unconcerned with the kind of God about which science can tell us.

Before accepting this reasoning, however, one fact should give us cause to think. If it is in any sense true that God created man— whether by a process of evolution or by a sudden creation—then God must be held responsible for the creation of what is in man and this must include man's sense of right and wrong: it must include our innate knowledge that the good is better than the bad.

For it will not do to suppose that God who Himself does not know the difference between good and evil should yet have made beings who are superior to Him in this respect. As well might we imagine a clockmaker who made a clock when he had no idea how a clock works. To reply that men do evil as well as good is beside the point—for they know, or are capable of knowing, that what they do is evil and no matter how they act, their inmost selves condemn the wrong decisions which they have made with their minds —decisions for which they, and sometimes others, are responsible.

Nevertheless, the idea that the Creator-God of science is amoral is now enormously prevalent with the result that, today, when study in the various fields of science is converging more than ever before to favour belief in God, men are less impressed by this united testimony than ever they were at a time when science had made little headway and natural theology was taken for granted.

The reason for this state of affairs is not difficult to discern. It is the result of an increasing awareness that nature is not wholly such as we might expect to find it, if it was, in fact, made by a moral Deity. There are ugly things to be explained and there is widespread doubt and disagreement as to the lines upon which an explanation should be sought.

Among the older school of theologians many take the line that in the presence of evil man finds himself confronted by an inscrutable mystery—a mystery that he must accept meekly and leave to his Maker for solution. Others, again, argue that, since the problem is insoluble (insoluble, even, if evil be ascribed to the devil, for that raises the problem: "Why does God allow the devil to disturb His plans?"), religious faith must be kept independent of natural theology.

To such views the sceptic angrily retorts that they beg the question at issue—the question as to whether a good and all-powerful God exists. For the believer to repudiate natural theology is, he says, with some justice, to adopt the ostrich-like policy of believing a theory and professing to be quite unconcerned about whether it fits the facts.

In view of the difficulty, we are asked, is it not simpler to suppose either (1) that there is an unperceived fallacy in all arguments which seem to lead to a belief in God, or (2) that God is real enough but that His nature is so far removed from man's as to be incomprehensible—so that it is meaningless to say that He is good, or (3) that God is real and personal but not almighty—that He like us is striving against evil forces in the cosmos?

Such are the main points of view that are put forward in our day. The subject has been discussed in books and articles, the numbers of which must run into tens, perhaps hundreds, of thousands. Perhaps mankind knows no corroding, haunting doubt comparable to this doubt—the evidence of the universe seems to point in both ways at once; to the goodness and badness of its Creator. The problem of evil makes a mock of man's reasoning powers and for ever tempts him to be cynical about his deepest religious yearnings. It is in this light, at least, that the problem appears to multitudes of contemporary men and women.

No adequate survey of the subject can be attempted in a few pages. But we may hope to draw attention to some of the main issues involved. Yet, since this book is concerned, primarily, with the lessons we may draw from science, we shall not attempt to discuss the more distinctly religious issues—such as the possible existence of a devil. For, whatever the grounds for belief in his existence may be (and they are not inconsiderable), the postulate of a devil must always appear *a priori* to the Naturalist who sees in this only an attempt to multiply hypotheses, to evade difficulties and to pry into the unknowable.

NATURAL EVILS

To clarify the issue, then, we may divide evil into two kinds— evil for which man is *not,* and evil for which he *is* directly responsible. Taking the former first, can we believe that a good God is responsible for hurricanes, volcanoes, avalanches, and earthquakes with the dreadful loss of life which they sometimes entail? Can we believe that God is responsible for cancer, malaria and tuberculosis—to say nothing of such minor ailments as the common cold? And what about the law of the jungle which we find in nature? Did God arrange that animals should prey upon one another for food? Is it of His ordinance that the cat plays with the mouse, that the lion tears the lamb to pieces, that the spider eats the fly? Do not these ugly facts of nature exactly neutralize any arguments that might be adduced to prove that God is good?

In thinking along this line it is easy to be persuaded by our own oratory—just as the ardent controversialist who sticks to his point, whatever betide, will, more often than not, come to believe in the point of view that at first he only accepted for the sake of a good argument. It is so here. Without in any way belittling what has been said, a case may be made for denying that the points we have mentioned are in any way typical of nature. In the words of a nineteenth-century writer—it is easy to be so concerned with the poor soul dying of cancer or consumption in a twelvemonth, as totally to ignore the preceding forty years of health and happiness

—just as if a man should ignore a mountain but profess himself awestruck by a mole-hill.[1]

Let us draw a comparison. What should we think of a party of undergraduates who, on being brought to an airfield to see a beautiful new airliner, came with their magnifying glasses and testing instruments and, without so much as looking at the airliner as a whole, proceeded forthwith to examine the ends of the ailerons, the wing surfaces and the tyres of the landing wheels for slight flaws—and, when they had found a few flaws of microscopic size, forthwith fell to dilating upon all the past instances in which airliners had crashed and killed their occupants as a result of flaws in the ailerons, wings and tyres? And what should we think of them if their leader then announced that it was their unanimous opinion that aeroplane makers are either (1) incompetent to make airliners or (2) are as wicked as devils for making them, since they never make them perfectly, and are, therefore, guilty of the death of all the persons who die in accidents?

Yet this, surely, is precisely the kind of argument which writers of today sometimes use about nature and God. The fact that, despite the amazing complexity of our bodies, despite the tens of thousands of things that *might* go wrong with us and yet do not go wrong, we are able for the most part to keep well and healthy—at least for by far the larger part of our lifetime—all this is overlooked. So also is the fact that those who have had to suffer pain, disability and infirmity, have often lived lives happily in the service of others.[2] Instead, the whole stress is placed upon the blemishes and the major facts are overlooked.

In the nineteenth century this attitude reached its climax. The existence of supposedly useless organs in the body—the appendix, for instance, or even an unnecessarily long intestine!—were exuberantly hailed as evidences that God had done His work badly. It is not so many years ago, too, that J. B. S. Haldane complained that if only his throat had been constructed on a different pattern he would never have choked.[3] Whether, such remarks are intended

---

[1] F. Ballard, *The Miracles of Unbelief*, 1901, 3rd ed., p. 76. This book, rarely read today, is a mine of interesting information.

[2] See, for example, *Disabilities and How to Live with Them*, published by *The Lancet*, 1952.

[3] "If my windpipe had been behind my gullet, instead of in front, I should never, or very rarely, have choked." J. B. S. Haldane *versus* A. Lunn. *Science and the Supernatural*, 1935, p. 174.

seriously it is difficult to say. They are reminiscent of the story of the physicist who, having cogitated long and carefully on the almost ideal properties of mercury as a means for removing heat in engines —it was liquid, he observed, had a low viscosity and a low freezing-point, unlike water it contracted instead of expanding on freezing, it had a high heat conductivity greatly superior to that of water, etc., etc.—forthwith filled the radiator on his car with the silvery metal. All went well—for a mile or two. But then the radiator fell off the car! The physicist had overlooked the great density of mercury, the sheer weight of which had removed the radiator bodily.

In the same way, criticisms of human anatomy may well be on a par with the suggestion that, say, human teeth would be better constructed of stainless steel than of bone. Perhaps they would— but steel teeth would not grow with age, nor can we well imagine how they might be handed on to a man's progeny!

The human frame, like the bodies of all animals, is a co-ordinated whole; it is easy to suggest improvements in parts but to carry out such suggestions would generally entail the destruction of that co-ordination upon which life and health depend.

Needless to say, the nineteenth-century attitude was riddled with inconsistency. On the one hand, men were told that science had to be purged of anthropomorphic conceptions (for if once these were allowed, the hypothesis of a God became well-nigh irresistible); on the other, they were assured that human feelings should be read into the lowest of animals and plants. Ignoring the co-operation that is a far more noticeable feature of nature than competition, scientists talked and wrote as if every fly caught in the spider's web suffered excruciating death agonies which put a tragic end to a painful and abortive existence. A universal struggle in which all nature was engaged was simply taken for granted. Darwin imagined that the very buds on the trees, even the atoms and molecules, were engaged in the ceaseless internecine warfare.

It is the legacy of this outlook which still haunts us today—for the ordinary man has never freed himself from this dark outlook despite the fact that historical investigation shows only too clearly that this whole movement of thought had its roots, not in an unpre-judiced study of nature, but in the popular theophobia of the day. It is only in the past few decades indeed, that the biologist himself has begun to find a way of escape from the shackles of this fault-finding attitude towards nature. But it must be added that it is not

Christians only who feel revolted by the "orthodox" nineteenth-century theories. Many non-Christians, too, cannot stomach the notion that nature seeks "to modify all things by blindly starving and murdering everything that is not lucky enough to survive in the universal struggle for hogwash," as Bernard Shaw puts it in *Back to Methusaleh*. In short, if we press home the argument that evil in nature disposes of the Christian God, we may have to go further and argue no less cogently that it disposes also of all decency and goodness, of all that gives to man a sense of nobility and worthwhileness. It may not do to argue that nature is unworthy of God and remain a humanist; if it is unworthy of God, perhaps it is unworthy of man too.

It is evident that we must look upon the so-called struggle in nature in a different light. And in fact we must view it in perspective, for it forms a part only of a wider problem.

STRUGGLE

The struggle which we see in nature confronts us in connexion with every contrivance, every force, with which we are familiar. Indeed, the more ingenious or the more potentially valuable a thing may be, the more easily does it become a menace when it is misused or permitted to get into its wrong place.

Rivers, for example, are of inestimable value—they irrigate the land, prevent flooding, provide water for towns, remove sewage, turn water-wheels, generate electricity, nourish fish, act as channels of communication and so on. Yet the more use man makes of them, the more does he become doomed to an everlasting "struggle" against them—waterways must be dredged, weeds must be removed periodically, dykes and locks kept in repair, the flow of water constantly controlled at numerous sluices, the oxygen content kept high, and the purity of factory effluents maintained. If any one of these matters is left unattended to, a river becomes not a blessing but a curse—devastating floods may menace homesteads and embankments, crops may be ruined, disease and famine may ravage the countryside, or fish may die.

It is the same with electricity. In proper control it is man's ally: out of control it is his enemy. Modern man is engaged—if again we choose to use the metaphor—in a constant "struggle" against electricity. Vast industries (those that make wire and insulators, for instance) are concerned only in the task of keeping it in the right channels—carelessness results in short circuit, fire, railway accidents, electrocution or factory explosion.

To all this, biology presents us with a close parallel. Here again we find repeated indications that man's struggle against nature is not, as a rule, a struggle against something evil, but a struggle to keep something potentially good and useful in the right place. Volcanic phenomena may be very terrible at the time of their occurrence—but earthquakes make the mountains while lava flows greatly increase soil fertility and, in the past, have given rise to some valuable minerals (pumice, vermiculite, bentonite).

In the past, perhaps, these analogies would have seemed far-fetched. Not so today. Evidence is rapidly accumulating that even disease organisms must be regarded much as we regard rivers or electricity.

At one time it must have seemed, perhaps, as if the disease-producing protozoa, bacteria and viruses were specially created to torture man and beast or to create disease in plants. No competent authority thinks in this way today. Of the origins of many of these micro-organisms and viruses we still know nothing. But in an increasing number of instances it has been found possible to discover the natural reservoirs of viruses. The classical example is that of the virus known as *Paracrinkle* which is an essential constituent of the King Edward potato—no such potato has ever been obtained free from it. Only when the virus enters some other host, such as the tomato, does it produce disease. The virus, in fact, is not a disease organism at all except when it leaves its normal habitat. Many viruses of which this is true are now known—so much so that workers in this field have coined the adage, "viruses in search of a disease". Such viruses will only cause deformity in another species if introduced by *grafting*, since there are no insect carriers. And it seems that they are essential to their hosts.

Turning now to protozoal and bacterial diseases the evidence is, though still fragmentary, much more complete. The microbes which inflict higher animals with suffering and disease were not created to do so—they are to be found living harmlessly, perhaps even beneficially, in countless animals, insects and plants, or living freely in jungle swamps.

Virulence appears, suddenly, when they are introduced into a host which is not their natural habitat. In Sumatra, in a region of jungle, never before visited by man, Zuelzer found a water leptospira which, on investigation, turned out to be identical with the microbe of Weil's disease. Pasteur found that the guinea pig carries chicken cholera, but is unharmed, perhaps even benefited by its presence. Numerous spirilla and vibrios grow in stagnant pools or, as saprophytes, inhabit the intestines of animals; spirochaetes, responsible for the scourge of venereal disease in man, harmlessly inhabit their hosts in the jungle. The wild beasts of the African forest harbour the sleepy sickness virus and are unharmed.

Something of the same kind is found even in ourselves. The colonies of bacteria that inhabit the large intestine are not useless—they carry out the synthesis of B vitamins from the indigestible residues of the food we eat. Among them, *bacillus coli* is a normal inhabitant—harmless and, like the others, probably useful. Yet introduced into the bladder or uterus, especially after childbirth, it at once becomes a danger to health.

Disease results, often enough, from changes in the host. In the tropics, native peoples are commonly infected with diphtheria, but the symptoms of the disease are unknown. In China, there are (or were) said to be places where scarcely a native intestine is devoid of a tapeworm, yet the natives are healthy, strong and happy. Artificial ways of living, inadequate or unbalanced diet may remove from man and animals alike the natural immunity with which they are endowed. Especially is this so as a result of psychological factors which, only too often, enable normal inhabitants of the body to become virulent.[1]

Thus the developing medical science of our day is putting the problem of disease in altogether a new light. Gone are the days when the sceptic could claim that there was as much evidence that God created the spirochaete as that He created the eye. Even the spirochaete may have its place in the world and if, out of that place, it has caused untold suffering to millions—the problem is no more unintelligible than the fact that misery results when, through carelessness or the taking of unnecessary risks, a plane falls on a house and kills the inhabitants or when a poison, intended for the garden weeds, is mistaken for medicine.

Again, we have already commented upon the fact that organization can lie hidden in a cell, all the cells of the body containing the

---

[1] On these newer ideas about the origin of disease, see, especially, the very interesting lecture by Dr. W. M. Levinthal, *Edinburgh Post-Graduate Lectures*, Vol. IV, 1948.

genes of the whole. Now just because the world contains self-duplicating nucleic-acid molecules, it may happen now and then that a portion of a chromosome will break off and start re-duplicating on its own account. It is in this light that many biologists regard viruses. And we must expect that these self-duplicating parts of organisms will occasionally evolve (unfold) new characters, just because they may still possess some of the hidden order of the original chromosomes from which they arose. When, therefore, they find themselves in new surroundings, in say the sap of plants or the blood of mammals, a chance mutation may bring to light some of the hidden structure they possess. Thus they will sometimes learn to generate chemical substances which prevent the formation of anti-bodies, for this secret is possessed by all organisms, otherwise they would destroy themselves.

In like manner free living organisms may occasionally degenerate by loss of some of their complex nucleic-acid equipment and become able, only, to live in conjunction with other living organisms upon which they become saphrophytic or parasitic. Once again, some of the hidden mechanisms may unfold, enabling newly-formed parasites to obtain a foothold. Since the adaptations will benefit the parasite they may seem to the onlooker ingenious and designed. So indeed they are—but the basic design belongs to earlier free-living organisms, rather than to the disease parasite of later days. It is in this light, no doubt, that we should regard the apparent ingenuity shown by the liver-fluke, the malarial parasite and the tapeworm. For biologists believe that such organisms are degenerate and, certainly, there is evidence that they and others like them were late on the scene in the history of life on earth.[1]

The subject, of course, is difficult, and our knowledge fragmentary. It is rarely possible to say, for certain, how an organism arose, or to account in detail for the apparent ingenuity of what may appear to us revolting. But to illustrate the point, let us consider what seems like the great ingenuity of the tapeworm in avoiding its own digestion in the alimentary canals of animals. It has discovered the secret of preventing enzymes from attacking its body, so that it remains unharmed while they carry out the

---

[1] "Parasitism of a pathogenic nature occurs only as early as the Devonian . . . Bacterial infectors are unknown until the late Paleozoic." "There are no known cases or examples of infection, no tumours, few traumatic lesions or injuries of any kind prior to the Devonian." R. L. Moody, *Palaeopathology* (Univ. of Illinois Press), 1923.

normal digestion of food. Was, then, an Almighty Designer so solicitous for the welfare of tapeworms that He created highly ingenious biochemical mechanisms to prevent their destruction? Or, even at a purely secular level, are we to believe that nature produces, *de novo*, the vilest machinery to destroy and harass her noblest creations?

It would seem not. Tapeworms are evidently degenerate creatures, now no longer capable of independent existence. But any free living organism must contain mechanisms which will prevent the digestion of proteins, for without them it would digest its own stomach and intestines. Even an amoeba is in some way protected from digesting itself. The genes necessary for the development of this mechanism must be present in the chromosomes, and they will be carried by all the cells of the body. As an organism develops from an egg, the mechanism will normally evolve only in the lining of the gut. But as a result of small random changes we can imagine that, by accident, it occasionally forms on the outside as well as the inside skin of some worm-like animal. When swallowed such an animal might continue to live. Further changes might follow, in all of which mechanisms *already present* in the genes would evolve, and the worm might become a tapeworm. There is ingenuity certainly, but the basic ingenuity is that of life itself, not of its parasitic development.

But, at this point, research in our day is revealing something of the amazing mechanisms to be found in nature which operate to prevent, or to hinder, the potentially virulent infector from gaining a hold where it might do harm. The wonders of immuno-chemistry as also of the body's power to remove harmful chemicals by turning into them harmless ones, have already been mentioned (Chap. X). Faced with such facts there can surely be but one reasonable reaction —a reaction not of pettifogging complaint that the wondrous mechanism is not designed to counteract an *infinite* number of harmful possibilities—no mechanism could possibly do that—but of wonder, adoration and thankfulness for the amazing wonders that we do find in nature.

There are some, of course, who will reply that these considerations are beside the mark. We shall be told that they will afford no comfort to the dying man who will still have to suffer just as if they had never been written.

This is true but it confuses the issue. Comfort comes from

religion, sympathy, companionship and help in time of need; alleviation from pain partly as a result of mental attitude and partly from the benefits of medical science. Thus far we have not been concerned directly to achieve either of these objectives. We have asked why men and animals *do* suffer—a matter of purely academic interest. We have found that, in the broadest terms, evil results when things which are harmless or useful get into the wrong places. And although this knowledge may fail to comfort us in suffering and certainly will not remove any suffering that we must bear, yet it must certainly react upon our attitude.

If we are injured by a car, we do not blame the makers of cars; if we cut ourselves with a knife we feel no malice towards the workmen who made it; if fire destroys a house, we do not blame the builders. In these and many other accidents, we do not let the frightfulness of the accident warp our judgement: we do not curse mankind for inventing cars, knives and houses. We are still able to see that these things are good in themselves and that those who make them confer great benefits on their fellow men.

It is the same with many natural calamities. The forest fire engulfs the wood-keeper's house in its blazing inferno—do we hear of men who blame God for making fire? Floods bring fearful devastation over the Chinese countryside—does the atheist assert that God was foolish to make water or to leave man without gills? Men are struck by lightning and killed, is electricity yet another of the Creator's colossal mistakes?

Even to ask these questions is to answer them—in the negative. But modern scientific discovery is teaching us that disease and suffering must generally be regarded in the same light as road accidents, fires, flooding and lightning. In the days of nineteenth-century ignorance, the atheist could make a plausible case for comparing cancer or malaria, not with electricity or the carving knife, but with the thumb-screw of the inquisition: today this comparison has lost its aptness. A steadily mounting mass of evidence is showing us that natural calamities, including disease, are only part of a much wider problem. And we are learning too that, whatever the ultimate reasons for maladjustment may be, earthquakes and disease afford us no more ground for impugning the goodness of the Creator than do fire and flood.

EVIL DONE BY MAN

When we turn to consider evil of the second kind—evil for which man is, directly or indirectly, responsible—we are confronted at once by a very striking fact. Modern knowledge is teaching us that man's responsibility is incomparably greater than was at one time supposed: that hundreds of evils which seemed at one time to be altogether outside his control are not really so at all but are often the results of culpable negligence and wickedness.

We have but to look back into the past to see the part that human sin has played in the dissemination of disease. Since the dawn of history, mass migrations of human beings, nearly always the result of conquering armies, have spread the world's microbes from country to country until, leaving their natural habitats, they have found new hosts in animals and men, so causing a gigantic total of suffering. Today we live in an age when there is a mix-up of micro-organisms such as has never been since life was upon earth. And the situation becomes steadily worse with every passing century—requiring all the resources of medical science to combat it.

Even in historic times, the situation was very different from what we find it today. In ancient Greece, the number of diseases known was very few. Malaria was not introduced until the fifth century B.C. when it became endemic and eventually caused the downfall of the country. Chest complaints, including pneumonia and tuberculosis, were also common. In addition typhus and bubonic plague probably visited the Mediterranean shores at long intervals and there is one record of mumps—a mysterious and unknown epidemic which attacked Thasos at the close of the fifth century, but seems never to have occurred again. Certainly there was little else—no diphtheria, scarlet fever, venereal disease, typhoid, smallpox, measles, chicken pox, or even influenza.[1]

The story has been much the same in many out of the way parts of the world in modern times. Native peoples have often lived relatively healthy lives until they have been decimated by diseases introduced by the whites—who have only too often come as conquerors.

It is probably no exaggeration to say that the vast majority of diseases in all ages have been introduced by war. In his inimitable

[1] W. H. S. Jones, *Malaria and Greek History*, 1909; *The Medical Writings of Anonymous Londinensis*, 1947, p. 159.

way Hans Zinsser[1] has told the story of how, all down history, military victories and defeats have resulted far more often from unexpected outbreaks of disease than from actual fighting; of how again and again conquering armies have spread new microbes through half-starved populations, slaughtering men in millions.

Nor is war the only way in which man has exhibited his cruelty and selfishness. The desire for wealth has, in our own century, resulted in the exploitation of the earth's resources to a degree unparalleled in history. In a few short decades we have seen whole continents drying up as a result of man-caused soil erosion; we have seen the creation of a million square miles of new deserts[2] with many millions more well on the way. We have seen, also, the extinction or near-extinction of numerous species of wild animals and birds which have been trapped or shot for fur, food or sport.[3]

In ancient times the Romans scoured Africa for strange beasts—elephants, lions and huge snakes—which they put to death in their arenas for the amusement of the populace.[4] To what degree their folly spread the world's microbes, to their own cost and to ours, we shall perhaps never know. Until recently we have carried on the tradition regarding it as a sport to murder the proud beasts of the forest and steppe in unfair combat with gunpowder and snare. The sufferings that man has inflicted upon innocent beasts, for purely selfish reasons, must beggar description. The gin trap, alone, has condemned hundreds of millions of happy free-living animals to a slow death—lasting a week or more—which has been aptly likened to crucifixion.

At times, even those elements in nature which men profess to find so revolting, have been vastly increased by man himself. Too often, as in the Spanish bull-fight, animals have been trained to kill one another for the mere fun of watching the spectacle. In his *Rich Cabinet*, John White, our own countryman, describes in the most matter-of-fact way "how to make dainty Sport with a Cat", by immersing its feet in molten pitch placed in walnut shells—such cruelties were once the order of the day.

---

[1] H. Zinsser, *Rats, Lice and History*, 1935.

[2] There has been widespread interest in this subject in recent years. Perhaps the best general reference is still G. V. Jacks and R. O. Whyte, *The Rape of the Earth*, 1939.

[3] McC. Moorehead, *No Room in the Ark*, 1959.

[4] G. Jennison, *Animals for Show and Pleasure in Ancient Rome*, Manchester University Press, 1937.

Again, until 1860 the wild baboons in Africa fed upon insects and roots. Then, as a result of careless agriculture and the determination to keep more cattle than the land could support, erosion set in on a nation-wide scale. The level of the great lakes fell, the smaller ones disappeared, humid forests with their trickling streams became parched grasslands and often, even, desert. Baboons, famished for water, commenced to attack goats, killing them to drink the milk in their udders. Later, they started to attack domestic animals of all sorts and to eat them for food. Slowly the new habit spread over the continent until, today, it is likely that not a tribe of baboons remains which continues to feed only upon the diet which had sustained their species for long ages past.[1]

Of the more obvious instances of the way in which man's sin and folly have produced suffering—of the famine, destruction, injury and death caused by war; of slavery and its industrial counterparts brought about by human covetousness and sadism; of the million selfish acts all down history which have brought their entail of suffering; of the countless murders (including that of Jesus Christ Himself) committed either out of hatred or for reasons of political expediency, there is no need to write. None are so ignorant as to be unaware of them.

MAN AT FAULT

It is impossible even to think along these lines without an ever-deepening sense of the sinfulness of man. But only too often men, realizing that they themselves are implicated (as indeed are all of us in greater or lesser degree) seek to make excuse. And the secular philosophy is one that makes excuse easy.

Often man is looked upon as a creature whose morals are evolving and who is to be congratulated for having come so far; often too, the stress is put, not upon the good that man might have done but has not done, but upon the fact that he might be worse than he is.

It is with this outlook that there can be no truce.

Whatever be our shade of opinion—religious or political—we all know that it is man's duty to order his life in accordance with the laws of nature. In trusting us with a material world God intended that we should use it with proper thought, just as those

[1] E. N. Marais, *My Friends the Baboons*, 1939, p. 1.

who make motor-cars and chemicals intend that their products should be used in a responsible way. To all this—though he may prefer to speak of nature in place of God—the secularist pays lip service readily enough. But, though there may be exceptions, in general his philosophy makes it impossible for him to take the challenge seriously. The thief and the murderer who refuse to admit that they have done wrong—who even congratulate themselves that they have not murdered or stolen more often—are unlikely to change their ways. A philosophy which minimizes or denies man's sin can never, in the last resort, help man to conquer his lust, his pride, his sloth, his hatred or his prejudice. It can never inspire man to make the best use of the potentialities which science has placed in his hands.

NATURE'S CRUELTY

To all this it might, of course, be retorted that whatever the blame that attaches to man, this is not the whole story. Long before man came upon the scene there was Darwinian struggle in nature—the strong did kill and eat the weak and predatory animals were so made that they could live by feeding one upon another. Can we imagine that a good God would have made them so?

To this we may, of course, reply that the struggle idea in biology has been grossly exaggerated and that the element of co-operation in nature is a much more marked feature than that of struggle. Nevertheless, it is certainly true that animals do prey upon one another for food, and the blame for this state of affairs most certainly cannot be placed upon man.

Yet, on this matter there is a surprising degree of misunderstanding. It is useless to complain that nature is made according to such and such a pattern unless we can suggest some better way in which it might have been made.

Suppose, then, that animals never ate one another but always died naturally. Would their suffering be less than it is? It certainly would not. The wounded and the infirm would linger on indefinitely in joyless existence, only to die of starvation when physically incapable of finding their food. But suppose animals were immortal —what then? The answer comes that over-multiplication would soon bring universal death from starvation. Alternatively, if they were immortal but had no progeny, accidents, frost or drought might cause the species to die out.

However we regard the matter, the conviction grows that the actual state of affairs that we find in nature is the only possible one —short of one in which, by special miracle, God healed every broken wing or brought a special dish of food to every animal unable to fend for itself—a possible state of affairs, no doubt, but hardly one conducive to character-making in man or beast.

We are, therefore, where we started. There is no reason to doubt that the present arrangement is the best possible. Perhaps a change to a régime of continuous miracle might be possible in an eternal state, when characters have been formed and men no longer choose to do evil, but hardly in our world.

Nevertheless, the present order is good. Nor have we any reason whatever to think that intense suffering is common in nature. Even if there were grounds for thinking that birds and mice, molested by cats, were as sensitive to pain as are we men, the suffering involved would be small. When the lion attacked Livingstone, biting through his arm, he felt little pain. In battle, severe pain is the exception rather than the rule. In World War II, two hundred and fifteen recently wounded men were questioned: less than a quarter had "bad pain"; the rest moderate, slight or none.[1] In times of danger adrenaline is at once poured into the blood-stream, and acts, apparently, as a general analgesic as well as a quickener of responses. The same hormone is manufactured by the adrenal glands of all higher animals.

It is interesting to note that the message of pain which travels along a nerve from a wound, does not itself produce more than a sense of discomfort when it reaches the higher brain. The emotion of pain is given to it on its way through the lower brain (the *hypothalamus*) and the function of drugs such as morphine is not to prevent the arrival of the messages but to prevent the lower brain from giving them the "interpretation" of pain in their passage. It seems that this lower region is much less developed in animals than in man, and even in man there are astonishing variations in the degree to which pain is found to be tolerable. Pain seems to be more intense in sensitive people and in those who think. Uneducated women sometimes deliver children almost

[1] See the interesting review of the subject by H. G. Wolff and D. Hardy in *Physiological Reviews*, 1947, **27**, 167.

painlessly and think nothing of it, but the suffering of the more sensitive is intense. Animals in the wild are more likely to resemble the former than the latter.

Pain has, of course, a definite and beneficial function. It is the warning that a wounded part of the body must not be used as if it were sound—given rest, the wound can heal and the broken bone rejoin. In the actual moment of danger, when life may depend upon sudden movement, pain is useless and therefore non-existent. It returns when the danger is over. If the wound is not severe, the pain is an important part of the healing process; if it is severe, the animal is incapacitated and is then rapidly and mercifully killed by its natural enemies.

Let us picture, then, the life of a wild animal. In its very early stages, before its nervous system has fully developed, it may be killed and eaten suddenly and painlessly. If it survives it develops skill and—as McNair Wilson[1] has so aptly pointed out—it then takes a natural pride in eluding its enemies, much as a reckless young man takes pride in crossing in front of the traffic, in jumping on and off moving buses, or in driving dangerously in a high-powered car.

By and by, either the animal has an accident or else old age creeps on. Then and only then does the predator get his chance. (A recent investigation showed that goats and other wild animals caught by lions in the natural state had all previously been incapacitated in some way.) The killing is normally instant but, even when it is not, excitement and passion make it painless.

In the rare instances when an animal escapes with a serious wound, it will certainly suffer pain when the excitement has subsided—but not for long since it will rapidly fall a prey at the next encounter. If the wound is slight, the pain also will be slight and may be followed by recovery.

In man, of course, such a life might well be described as evil. But only on account of his ability to think. Animals are not haunted by doubts of what the morrow may bring, nor of the needs of the surviving members of their families should they be killed in combat. Nor again do they experience the intense sufferings of bereavement when their kith and kin are lost—among a few species they wilt for a while, some more than others, but memories are short.

This is the worst that we can say about nature. But predators are by no means the only causes of death. Inclemencies of the weather

[1] R. McNair Wilson, *The Witness of Science*, 1942

take a heavy toll. When age creeps on, the old penguin leaves the other birds and retires to the mountains alone, there quietly allowing the frost to numb and kill her. The physical suffering involved in such a death can hardly be great—Arctic explorers describe how, when tired, it is all they can do to muster enough will-power to avoid the peaceful, painless sleep that knows no awakening.

Sir Joseph Barcroft, as a result of experimenting upon himself, tells us that the first sensations of cold disappear after a time and are replaced by a sensation of pleasant warmth, at which point, however, the temperature of the body begins to fall rapidly so that death must soon ensue if the experiment is not terminated.

Starvation, too, in man leads after a few days to a long period of lethargy in which food is not even desired—only near the end is pain again experienced. Thirst may be much more painful but water is abundant in nature—or was, until man the desert-maker came upon the scene.

Yet we have still been thinking only of death and disease—which are by no means typical of the natural order. Animals know far more of happiness than of fear and pain if appearances mean anything—and if they do not, of course, no problem arises. The lioness playing with her cubs, the cat purring by the fire, the birds building their nests, the squirrels darting from tree to tree—all those sights and a thousand more spoke to former generations of joy and carelessness at the heart of nature. It is hard to believe that the old interpretation is altogether wrong.

Is the picture we have painted one of "teeth and talons whetted for slaughter, hooks and suckers moulded for torment—everywhere a reign of terror, hunger, sickness, with oozing blood and quivering limbs, with gasping breath and eyes of innocence that dimly close in deaths of cruel torture," to quote the words of G. J. Romanes? Surely not. Such an interpretation is more suggestive of a perverted imagination than of a sober appraisal of facts. It is difficult to believe that the use of such language is more realistic than the behaviour of Nero who, entranced by the beauty of the flames of burning Rome, donned his comedian's robes and sang an opera perched on the tower of Maecenas.

The biologist who could write like this was blind in more senses than one—the claws that he thought were red with blood were often green with chlorophyll (Wheeler): the hooks and suckers were not moulded for torment but mercifully provided with analgesics and anaesthetics; the reign of terror was a life of carefree happiness and defiance of potential enemies.

MAN'S ESTIMATE

But if, despite all, we remain sceptical concerning the Biblical statement that "God saw everything that He had made, and behold it was very good", we must not forget that this, too, is the final verdict of *man*.

The world-wide desire to ban atomic war arises from the conviction, surely, that the world is worth saving. If men *really* thought, that the world was an evil creation, would they go to such pains to save it? Would it not be more sensible to let events run their course and if all life was annihilated as a result of man's stupidity—well, would it matter much?

In the same way all thinking men—Christian and non-Christian alike—are convinced that it would be a tragedy if species were to continue to become exterminated as has happened in recent history. Again why? If the struggle for existence makes animal life evil and cruel—would it not be kinder to let the rarer species die out instead of bothering to preserve them?

Deep down in our minds, whatever we may *say*, it is reasonable to believe that our verdict is the verdict of God, "behold it was very good." And if that be so, whatever the difficulties, the problem of evil cannot be insuperable.

Can we then imagine that nature is the handiwork of a good and loving God? Why not?

In a recently published book (*A Scientist who Believes in God*, Hodders, 1961) Dr. H. N. V. Temperley outlines the arguments which led him, as an agnostic, to become a Christian. In Dr. Temperley's view Christians in the past have made the mistake of comparing the world to a *finished* article, such as the proverbial Paley's watch. Despite the strong evidence of design in nature, the existence of evil makes this hypothesis inadequate. When we encounter difficulties in science, the usual procedure is to modify our hypothesis. Let us suppose, then, that the universe is not complete but is still being fashioned—let us liken it to a factory continually adapting itself to the needs of consumers, rather than to a watch. In this way we can account for most of what we call "evil" quite easily. In a changing situation many right decisions made by a good management will inevitably appear wasteful and harmful.

CHAPTER XVII

TWO PHILOSOPHIES

THROUGHOUT this book we have been concerned with two ways of thinking; two approaches to truth; two philosophies. In this, our closing chapter, we shall attempt to clarify the differences between them and to draw the threads of our argument together.

NATURALISM

The first philosophy is the philosophy of Naturalism. It seeks to make nature the yardstick of reality. And by nature is meant the subject-matter of science—the material world of physics and biology, together with the mental world of psychology. This naturalistic philosophy is often called materialism. And though we have sometimes used the word it is, strictly speaking, unjustified, for neither the various field concepts of physics nor the thoughts and feelings of the human mind can by any stretch of imagination be called *material*. Nevertheless, Naturalism is a logical development of nineteenth-century materialism, so that the appellation is not altogether unjust.

What, then, is the evidence upon which the Naturalist seeks to establish his case? He argues that nature provides us with no convincing evidence that cosmic Mind is operating upon the world today. The existence of such a Mind cannot, of course, be disproved. But the regularity and reliability of physical law seems to show that Mind is not normally intervening. Furthermore, even if certain modern physicists are right in their claim that chance lies at the back of law, it still remains clear that nature is not governed by an all-wise overruling intelligence. God, therefore, is an unnecessary hypothesis—natural enough, perhaps, in the age of faith when man was ignorant of science, but wholly out of place today.

Plan, purpose and mind are, therefore, concepts meaningful

enough for man who is possessed of a complex brain, but mere
mythology when they are projected on to nature. Instead of
imagining a spirit world, we should try to realize that the property
of thinking is like, say, the property of sewing possessed by a
sewing-machine—a property which emerges at a certain level of
the organization of its parts, but which is completely non-existent
before that level is reached.

So the Naturalist assures us that a scientific philosophy must take
into account the fact that man lives in a universe the forces of
which are totally unrelated to his desires, needs and aspirations.
He has developed the power to think as a result of a long evolutionary struggle with his environment and, now that he is possessed
of self-consciousness, he realizes that he is alone in the scheme of
things. Mental powers, such as his own, are unknown anywhere
else in nature. There are conceivably other man-like beings in far
away worlds but, if so, their very distance can only serve to increase
man's sense of utter loneliness and isolation. The things that man
treasures most dearly—love, beauty and even morality—are things
that he possesses alone. Nature refuses to share them with him:
carelessly and ceaselessly she shows her utter disregard of them.
Disease drags loved ones to the grave; earthquakes destroy cities;
cold and heat bring their hardship. Nature is cruel, mechanical,
ruthless and her laws show no favouritism between the parasite and
its host, between human devils and human angels. Man finds himself alone, condemned to struggle unequally against natural forces.
To preserve his values he must wage relentless war against nature,
harnessing her powers to his needs. In this strife he must rely upon
himself alone, for there is no one else to help him.

Above all, it is important that man should entertain no ideas
which might unfit him for his struggle. Most dangerous of all such
ideas is the dogma of sin—the Christian doctrine that man is a
pitiable sinner whose duty it is to repent. The Naturalist cannot
afford to tolerate this teaching. With pathetic earnestness he realizes
that if man fails in the struggle to which he is doomed, the race of
mankind will die out and nothing, not even a memory, will be left
behind. Repentance and tears are out of place on a battle-field.

Such is the so-called scientific philosophy of the Naturalist. It
has been expounded by many writers but by none of them, perhaps,
more movingly than by Sir Charles Sherrington.[1] In his well-

[1] *Man on His Nature*, 1940, especially pp. 384, 402.

known Gifford Lectures, Sherrington argued that, with the coming
of modern science, the old design argument ceased to have meaning. Man's physical isolation from the forces of nature are of
themselves enough to make him lonely. Yet his loneliness, says Sir
Charles, is greatly increased by yet another consideration. He is
lonely at home. "No other mind his equal, let alone superior to it.
All other minds its inferior, and almost incompanionably so. His
thinking is thus thrown utterly upon itself." And so man's mind is
left, "grappling with its newly found 'values,' yet with no experience except its own, no judgement but its own, no counsel but its
own. None to seek guidance from. None of whom to ask a
question." Never in history has any creature been allotted so lonely
a place in the universe as modern man. His spirit "yearns for
company, comradeship, angels—even demons", but there is no
response. Bravely he must accept his lot. He must try to build a
religion, or a substitute for religion, upon the only truth he knows
—the truth of science. True, such a religion is bound to fall far
short of what men once believed. It can never be charged with the
emotional content of a faith that professes to enable man to know
God. Yet not everything is lost. Truth and Beauty will provide
passion : emotions will be stirred as attempts are made to conquer
nature. No longer able to ask counsel of a higher mind in our
perplexities, we cannot help seeing in our position an element of
enhanced tragedy and pathos. Yet the task before us is one "which
transforms the human spirit's task, almost beyond recognition, to
one of loftier responsibility" than any it has known before.

Sentiments less eloquent indeed, but alike in kind to these, have
been expressed by a hundred lesser writers. One and all make the
same assumptions and say the same things. Science, we are told,
has destroyed the old theological outlook on nature; it has trained
us to ask how and not why; it has left us alone in the universe to
stand or fall as we please, to take charge of our own destiny or to
refuse to do so. And there is generally a rider to the effect that we
must no longer look upon ourselves as "miserable sinners", but
must rise up and realize our dignity and importance.

So much for the naturalist position. Now let us examine it in
more detail. We have already noted that despite his claim to be
scientific, the Naturalist only reaches his conclusions because he
argues in a way that is the very reverse of orthodox scientific procedure. Instead of studying the odd, the exceptional and the

suggestive, he thinks only of the ordinary and commonplace. And he fails to see that, in so doing, he assumes what he wishes to prove; for he selects from nature the part that is consistent with his pre-formed philosophy of naturalism.

Moreover, it must at once be obvious that an attempt to discover whether there is an answering counterpart to our own minds in nature, can never be settled by an examination of natural processes that are taking place at the present time. For the principles known to science are very numerous. Even were we to concentrate atten-tion upon rather rare and unusual phenomena, it would always be difficult to build a logically sound case—one way or the other. It is almost impossible to suggest any kind of event, real or imaginary, for which a naturalistic explanation could not be suggested. Imagine, for example, a modern Daniel in a modern lions' den. If Daniel was not eaten by the lions it *might*, of course, be a miracle. But it might be because the lions were not hungry, or because the people who ran the show had placed an invisible screen between Daniel and the lions, or because Daniel was not really in the den at all but his image, visible to the outsider but invisible to the lions, had been thrown into the den by the method of the Dirksian phantasmagora; or the lions might have been conditioned by a Pavlovian technique not to eat Daniel for their supper; being connected invisibly to an electric machine so that they got a shock when they started to eat him; or . . . And if it so happened that competent scientists and technicians were on the spot, equipped with all necessary instruments to discount these and other sugges-tions—well—what evidence was there that the event really took place as recorded? How do we know that the eye-witnesses were reliable? Did they write the story on the spot or did they wait for time to play tricks with their memories? How can we be sure that collective hallucination will not account for the appearance? . . . And so on.

Such objections can always be made in an almost limitless stream to every supposedly miraculous occurrence. It would be difficult to find, even to imagine, any event in history which would prove to the Naturalist that his own principle of Naturalism had broken down. And this the Naturalist knows very well and exploits to the full. That is why he insists that a scientific philosophy must be based upon an examination of current everyday happenings. And so, consciously or unconsciously, he fences himself in where no

evidence can touch him and then glories in his security, conveniently
forgetting that he is only safe because he refuses to meet his enemy;
that the kind of evidence which he demands to convince him is the
kind which, from the nature of the case, can never do so.
Naturalism, in short, is a cheat. It professes an open mind, but its
mind is closed; it professes the scientific method, but repudiates it
in practice; it professes to build a philosophy on the science of our
day, but only appears to do so because it carefully selects evidence
of a kind that can never settle the point at issue.

THE APPEAL OF NATURALISM

Why, then, has naturalism obtained so wide a hearing? Why is
it that it sometimes appeals, even, to men of great brilliance
and ability? This question we have already answered in part.
Naturalism arises from the proverbial missing of the wood for the
trees. If we pay detailed attention to an isolated part of some
machine or of some process, we find it difficult to realize that the
part is essential to the whole. The hands of the skilled glass-blower
move and even shake in such a manner as to make an onlooker
think that he is careless—yet the seemingly random movements are
co-ordinated to a surprising degree. Considered in isolation, the
muscular contractions involved in the putting on of a shirt seem
almost at random—yet they are ordered with an end in view. In
the same way we have seen that those who fail to recognize that
there is order in nature, those who even deny its existence, are the
specialists whose whole attention is directed towards the investigation of some one group of natural phenomena. True, such men are
occasionally clever enough, even outstandingly brilliant in their own
line, yet they naturally tend to regard as exceptional the examples
of order which their own studies provide. These they proceed to
explain away, oblivious of the fact that they constitute examples of
a universal principle that is to be found throughout the whole of
nature. And this being so, it is not difficult to understand why a
certain class of scientists is so emphatic in its endorsement of
naturalistic views. There is a vicious circle involved, too, for the
more the specialist specializes, the more inclined does he become to
build his philosophy upon that limited branch of knowledge on
which he is an authority and the less is he tempted to invoke
principles which do not find a place in that science.

The appeal of naturalism outside strictly scientific circles is easily understood on the same lines. Modern scientific education— even at its lower level—is notoriously specialized with the result that the same factors which operate in the specialist scientist often operate, even more dangerously, in the lay mind. The extraordinary tendency of specialized science to divert attention away from the really important issues and to focus it upon mere trivialities instead, must be obvious to all who are familiar with modern text-books. A single example will suffice. The student of physics learns about such topics as variations in the earths magnetic field with latitude, the earths magnetic poles, isobars, isochores, magnetic storms and so on. He learns, too, about the ways in which the earth's magnetic field interacts with bar magnets, with moving wires, rivers, etc. All is important and interesting, but the fundamental point—why has the earth a magnetic field at all?—is either ignored or dismissed in a sentence. The reason is that there is not as yet, or was not, until recently, a generally accepted theory on the subject—a fact which is no fault of the teacher. Yet an education which fails to stimulate the mind to concern itself with fundamental issues; which stresses only a detailed knowledge of the froth of nature and asks no questions about the waters below—can hardly lead to an outlook that is unwarped. It is as if a sailor were to spend a lifetime study-ing the movements of his ship, constructing precise mathematical formulae to describe the regularities of the pitching and rolling, but was totally unconcerned with the fact that his ship was buoyed up by the sea. It is specialization of this kind which distorts the outlook of today : trained in such grooves of thought, men tend to build philosophies as inconsequential as the crumbs of science which they pick up from their teachers.

It is no cause for wonder, then, that many moderns fail to see purpose in life or in the universe. The naturalism of today is in no way a matter for surprise but follows exactly along the lines that any intelligent person might have anticipated. Comenius did, in fact, anticipate it as far back as in the seventeenth century.

The fundamental shakiness of the naturalist position is demon-strated in no better way than by the weakness of the arguments which the Naturalist uses in self-defence. He resents every attempt to analyse the situation critically; he confines technical discussion to some narrow issue (such as a possible chance self-winding of the universe or the existence of evil) and, when faced with positive evidence of the incorrectness of his views, instead of challenging the facts or their interpretation he indulges, instead, in belligerent polemics. Thus, he often roundly accuses his opponents of believing superstitious nonsense, of returning to primitive beliefs, of putting the clock back or (as some Freudians might say) of returning to the phantasies of the nursery. Knowing that reason is not on his side, he seeks to stir up prejudice against his opponent's views.

THE EVIDENCE

How, then, may a valid philosophy be based upon modern science? First and foremost we must free our minds from prejudice. Unlike the Naturalist we must not tacitly assume what we wish to prove but must be willing to examine the evidence fairly with a desire to learn from it. And secondly—as has already been noted in the Introduction—we must examine especially, not the everyday and ordinary, the established laws of science, but the odd, unusual and suggestive features of our universe. For we shall learn nothing new if we think, merely, about what we already know. Analysis of sea-water in a test-tube will not tell us if there are sea-serpents; analysis of the known laws and principles of laboratory science will not tell us whether the whole of nature can be interpreted upon naturalistic lines.

Our purpose in this book has been to investigate some of the points which increasingly strike us as odd the more science advances our understanding of nature. We started, first of all, by considering one of the queerest and most baffling enigmas with which science confronts us—that of the steady running down of the entropy clock of the universe and the logical corollary that the clock must once have been wound up. (And the logic of the argument was not altered if a 'steady-state' theory of the Universe was adopted.)

We learned that the world cannot have been created in the first place by the operation of the ordinary laws of science which we can see working themselves out today. The idea of the Maxwellian "demon" suggested, though perhaps it did little more than suggest, that the origin of the universe might have been connected with a mind-like force or power. But, more important still, the fact of a creation epoch suggested that all science was, in a sense, superficial.

For the science that we study is only the running down, so to speak, of the clock and to profess interest in the running down but not in the winding up, is to be every bit as superficial as to profess interest in the slight variations in the earth's magnetism but not in why the earth is a magnet at all.

Next, we considered the solar system. We learned that our earth, far from being the kind of planet which we should expect to result from chance, appears to be one in which a number of distinctive features have combined to make it a suitable abode for life.

Considering this fact in isolation, it was possible to take the view that, since the earth happens by chance to be habitable, man is here to tell the tale. Otherwise we men would not exist. That sounded plausible enough but was there, perhaps, another way of regarding the matter? The facts could be explained equally well, perhaps better, on the view that there was a plan behind nature—a plan which entropy had already suggested to our minds.

On turning to chemistry, we found positive confirmation that the plan theory was correct. For the chance hypothesis now proved much less plausible than before.

Chemistry revealed an astonishing array of facts which had all the appearance of having been designed according to a plan. The properties of a number of the elements fitted exactly into the pattern of what was required for living matter. The remarkable properties of water and of carbon dioxide which had been known for a long time fitted into a teleological picture of nature. Recent research enormously increased the cogency of this chemical argument—by showing that a number of other elements and compounds also possess remarkable and unexpected properties which enable them to take part in the chemical processes of living matter.

The evidence of plan was beginning to mount. It seemed reasonable, in view of what we had discovered, to go back and interpret the astronomical facts in terms of this plan.

At this point we turned to consider the biological evidence. The attempt to explain away biological order by chance upon which natural selection had operated proved hopeless upon examination. Simple and wonderful biochemical mechanisms were to be found in the lowliest as in the highest form of life. Evidence that they had evolved *de novo* was lacking and such a suggestion seemed, in any case, unlikely. The nature of the basic reactions, necessary for all life, was such as to indicate with scarcely a loophole for doubt, that living cells could not have arisen from non-living matter by chance. Faced by the undeniable existence of almost inconceivably complex and ingenious chemical mechanisms, the conclusion once again seemed irresistible that they were the results of design. This conclusion became even more difficult to avoid when, in a subsequent chapter, we learned that very many human inventions, which seemed to show human ingenuity at its height, had long before been anticipated in nature.

In addition to these arguments, which we discussed in greater detail in the earlier part of this book, we have also had occasion to refer to an argument of a different kind—based, this time, upon mathematical physics. One of the most characteristic features of research in this field over the past few decades has been the fact that, not once but repeatedly, physicists have been able to confirm the predictions of the theoreticians. In this way new particles (positrons, mesons, etc.) have been discovered, together with a number of surprising new physical phenomena. It seems to follow, then, that the physical world has been constructed in such a way that it is related to the *thoughts* of men. This astonishing discovery has been the subject of much discussion but, once again, it seems to indicate that our own minds are not alone in nature. For, if the laws of thought find a reflection in the physical world, how can we believe that the physical world came into existence without thought? It was by reasoning along these lines that Jeans came to the conclusion that God was a "pure mathematician"—a somewhat parochial outlook, perhaps, but surely one not wholly devoid of truth.

Modern mathematical physics has also done much to show that the cocksure attitude of the old-fashioned scientist has no sound foundation. In the last resort it becomes impossible to prove, even, that most self-evident of all physical postulates—causality. Matter, energy, electricity, gravitation—one and all seem to pass beyond physical understanding into a realm of mathematics when once they are probed with sufficient care. This fact, even if it does not lend direct support to natural theology, is enough to remove many of the difficulties which were once thought to be formidable.

INTERPRETATION

So much for the evidence. We turn now to its interpretation. Firstly, we saw that it was impossible, or at least extremely difficult, to avoid the conclusion that the plan of the universe was due to a Mind behind it—a mind separate from nature but able to act upon nature from without. We considered whether or no this Mind could be regarded as personal and were forced to answer the question in the affirmative. Furthermore, in view of the fact that He has brought into existence man, who recognizes that good is better than evil even when he follows evil, it seemed natural to suppose that He was moral. In saying this we recognized the danger of "making God in our own image"—we realized that God might be something far beyond our powers of conception. Personality and morality might, then, be something much *less* than His being, but at least they were part of it, the part intelligible to us.

Next we considered two possible lines of objection. Firstly, there was the argument that a philosophy based upon current science was unsatisfactory, since science might at some future date lead to another conclusion. In answer to this we explored the history of the subject, only to find that the best science of every age has led thinkers to the same or a very similar conclusion. It was reasonable, therefore, to hold that our conclusion was based upon a residuum of fact so solid that it was likely to remain unchanged throughout all time.

Secondly, we observed that the vast majority of thinking people would be willing enough to accept our conclusion, were it not that the existence of evil raises doubts concerning the goodness of God.

We turned, therefore, to consider the nature of evil, only to learn with surprise that the usual agnostic arguments based upon its existence are applied so inconsistently and haphazardly as to carry little weight. A rapid survey of recent scientific researches which bear on the subject revealed the fact that, in general, evil arises when potentially good things are misplaced. It appeared that many misplacements are, or were at one time, the fault of man. The evidence suggested that the argument that the Creator is not good because He made the malarial plasmodium was probably comparable to blaming Him for making water because rivers sometimes go into flood.

From this bare outline of the arguments and conclusions of earlier chapters we begin to see the emergence of the beautiful and satisfying world-picture that is revealed to us by modern science—a picture which, though it resembles the pictures which have been painted in days gone by, is more convincing, more beautiful, more satisfying and more self-consistent than any of its predecessors.

The new world-picture bears little resemblance to the isolated and fragmentary pictures which are painted by Naturalists of the ephemeral nineteenth-century tradition. For a wide survey of science reveals the fact that Mind is not a thing that developed for the first time in the universe at the end of a long evolutionary process: rather it is something that lies at the core of the universe—something without which there would be no universe. There was mind before there was man and there would still be mind were man, as man, to exist no more. The doctrine that man is alone in the universe is, therefore, false; he is very far from being alone. Turn where we please, on every side we see the evidences of Mind. With matchless wisdom and power Mind has made the world, having evidently expended upon it a degree of thought so stupendous that, to us, it is as incomprehensible as astronomical distances or periods of time. The quality of that thought we can understand—it is the sheer vastness of the co-ordination that it has brought about that inevitably brings to us a feeling of our own utter insignificance. Before such Intellect, such ingenuity, such planning, we can only feel that our mental stature is as small as our physical stature seemed to be when first we learnt about the distance of the stars. In such a universe, man can no more boast of his intellectual powers than he can boast of his physical size.

Perhaps we may go on a step further. The idea that nature is intelligible to man is fundamental to science. There are many things in nature that we cannot understand; many phenomena, which seem to contradict all known laws. It would be easy to "throw up the sponge" as it were—to argue that it is silly to believe in the theory of gravitation because Mercury does not keep to its proper orbit, or to believe in the conservation of energy because objects move in haunted houses. It is a matter of faith among scientists that the universe is rational and that is why, when confronted with a difficult problem, they do not at once lose confidence and begin to question whether the universe is orderly after all.

But science itself has now shown us that the orderliness of nature is not ultimately confined to the kind of orderliness with which physical science deals. In addition to that part of nature that is orderly in the sense that it can be described by means of mathematical equations, much is purposively or teleologically orderly—and this teleological element is, as we have seen, extremely widespread and at least as important as the part that is determined by physical law. It is this teleological orderliness, in fact, which enables us to collate an immense number of what would otherwise be isolated facts—to see their meaning in the light of the whole.

What attitude, then, are we to adopt when—as is bound to happen occasionally—we are faced by apparent facts which seem to upset the universal orderliness? How are we to interpret the fact of evil? To this question there can surely be but one answer—we must exercise a faith identical in kind to that faith which every scientist adopts when he is confronted by the inexplicable. We have seen that, even ignoring theological possibilities (such as the possible existence of an evil mind or devil of limited power in opposition to God), evil is by no means a proof of ultimate disorderliness in the structure of the world. True, it could be so interpreted. But science has shown us that other explanations are also possible. Since the Naturalist is, of all people, the most child-like in exercising a faith similar to the one we are considering, he can scarcely complain if we decide to believe that the universe makes moral as well as intellectual sense. In short—God is good.

Here, then, is our theory—and it is one that gives us a wonderfully satisfying picture of the world. But good theories, developed as a result of studies in obscure fields, have an uncanny habit of changing our vision of the ordinary and commonplace. Studies of the rare property of magnetism have thrown light upon the structure of ordinary non-magnetic substances; study of a queer and only just detectable property of pitchblende led, in the end, to our knowledge of the structures of all atoms. And so it is here. Our conclusions relating to obscure and remote events in the history of our universe and of our earth, throw a flood of light upon the common work-a-day world.

For the conclusion is surely irresistible that a God, so wonderful, so mighty, so good has not simply disappeared out of the universe that He made. True, we have great difficulty in producing a cast-iron argument that He is intelligently at work in the world today but, remembering our analogy of Daniel and the lion's den, this need cause us no astonishment.

TEACHING OF JESUS

At this point we enter the field of religion—a subject with which this book is not primarily concerned. But it would be folly indeed to close without reference to the line of reasoning which Jesus employed in speaking to the multitudes.

Christ taught that, by watching the course of nature, men could learn about the character of God.

> Behold the birds of the heaven, that they sow not, neither do they reap, nor gather into barns; and your heavenly Father feedeth them. Are not ye of much more value than they? . . . Consider the lilies of the field, how they grow; they toil not, neither do they spin; yet I say unto you, that even Solomon in all his glory was not arrayed like one of these. But if God doth so clothe the grass of the field, which today is, and tomorrow is cast into the oven, shall He not much more clothe you, O ye of little faith?

It is evident that for Jesus, nature was no shambles but the gateway into the presence of its Creator: alone in the hills He met God in prayer and after the days of His tempting He remained with the wild beasts. Evidently He saw the providence of God in the fact that the foxes had their holes and the birds of the air their nests.

Lessons might be learnt even from the inorganic world:

> Love your enemies, and pray for them that persecute you: that ye may be sons of your Father which is in heaven: for He maketh His sun to rise on the evil and the good, and sendeth rain on the just and the unjust.

Or, to put the argument in other words, God has so ordered nature that the blessings of sun and rain, heat and cold, come upon all men alike. Yet how easily it might have been otherwise—how easily God might have created a world in which sin was immediately punished. God, then, must be merciful. It cannot be His will to destroy sinners but to give them every chance to repent. God, therefore, loves His enemies; and men too, if they would become sons of their Father who is in heaven, must love their enemies and pray for them. That is how Jesus argued—and it is evident that He expected His hearers to follow the argument.

To us, perhaps, these arguments sound strange, other-worldly and unconvincing. Even Christians are sometimes half ashamed of them: they try to persuade themselves that Jesus was not using arguments at all but was merely drawing attention to analogies between nature and the spiritual world. The arguments seem, at first sight, utterly contrary to what we have learned from science. Science seems to tell us that it is not God but genes which clothe the lilies and impart to the birds their pecking instincts. And as for the argument that sunshine and rain benefit good and bad alike—well—we are tempted to retort that the facts might equally well be interpreted to mean that nature is indifferent to good and evil.

But these objections arise only because men insist on treating certain facts of nature in isolation. To stress the fact that the forms of plants and the instincts of birds are inherited is to forget the all-important fact that God endowed them all with royal munificence: that the wealth of care—which extended even to endowing plants with beauty and animals with instincts—to be seen in nature is prodigious. The thought that must have been involved in the making of the human body—far more complex than the bodies of plants and birds—is unimaginable. We know something of the prodigious mental effort required in the making of a serviceable aeroplane or piece of electronic equipment. As complexity rises, so the degree of co-ordination required increases far more rapidly than the mere number of parts would lead us to suppose. But the human body is of a complexity unimaginable to man. It must contain, in all, thousands, even millions, of ingenious devices, each one co-ordinated with the others to make up the whole. True, the pattern once made reproduces itself. But that does not mean the individual is unimportant. Even if we take all the human beings who have lived (scarcely much above ten or fifteen thousand million) and assume that all have been produced mechanically from the beginning, there would still be an average of no mean amount of thought for each.

And since we know that throughout nature God has attended to the most minute details, it becomes pointless to say that, because nature is not constructed in such a way that wrongdoers are immediately punished, God is indifferent to the distinction between right and wrong. The mere fact that He made man's mind, which recognizes this distinction, is sufficient refutation of such a view. Obviously God had a motive in what He did. And the obvious motive is the one which Christ pointed out—that God wanted evil men to become good.

The subject, however, is hardly one that can be exhausted in a few paragraphs. Suffice it to say that the picture of the world which we are gaining today as a result of advances in one field of science after another, is one that is making the intuitions and arguments used by Jesus Christ far more plausible and more cogent than ever they were in the so-called age of faith.

OTHER WORLDS?

We have collected the threads together so far as the evidence warrants. But, inevitably, curiosity prompts us to ask more questions than we can answer.

What is the purpose of the universe? Is its function to bring life into existence? Are we the only thinking creatures? Or are there, at this moment, other inhabited worlds where man-like creatures work and think and pray? Are there any facts to guide us in such speculations?

A few perhaps. Astronomy reveals the resources of nature in limitless profusion. Man needs to practice economy: but economy becomes meaningless if resources are infinite. You need not bother about the efficiency of the gears of your car if petrol costs *nothing*, not even the trouble of filling the tank.

If then, a vast universe had been brought into existence for the benefit of a few inhabited worlds, perhaps only *one*, it would be quite wrong to befog the issue by talk of wastefulness.

And if we ask *how* distant galaxies can possibly benefit man, one part of the answer is probably this—that without those distant galaxies there would be no gravity, matter would possess no mass (inertia), centrifugal force would be non-existent, planets would not gyrate, worlds such as ours would be impossible. (See p. 184). If we are tempted to retort that our galaxy is merely one of countless millions, just like the rest, we need reminding that on the contrary it seems to be one of a most unusual type, very large and possessed of several centres instead of the usual *one* (though how significant such features may be, we simply do *not* know).

In biology we see a rather similar situation. Since matter and energy on the earth's surface are limited, they are conserved and waste is avoided. But not so with organization. A million acorns give one oak, thousands of millions of ova and sperm give a single individual, of millions of baby fish swarming the seas, only a few survive. There is no waste of matter here for seeds, eggs and little fishes are food for adults, but there is profligate over-production of organization.

We note the same feature when we think of different *types* of organization. For the different species run into millions, especially among insects and plants. Though it might have been less interesting, the world could certainly have existed with fewer.

Concomitant with this apparent waste there is selectiveness. Man is unique. Of all the species, only he can think abstractly. Only he can develop civilizations. And he is selected in time, too. He has existed only for a tiny fraction of the time that life has been on earth. In the age of the reptiles, there was no man to till the soil. Or again, the solar system contains many planets and satellites: only one is suitable for advanced life.

A high degree of selectiveness confers a sense of value. The picture chosen from a multitude of pictures, the precious mineral specimen, coral, or butterfly discovered and selected from thousands by the collector seem to him possessed of value. It is reasonable to think that God looks upon man in the same way.

But selectiveness shows itself in another way, too. It has often been said that of all the leaves on a tree no two are the same; of all the blades of grass in a field, each one is different. And, of course, of all the thousands of millions of human beings who have lived, no two were quite the same.

Suppose, then, that on unseen planets gyrating around stars in distant galaxies there are other thinking beings beside ourselves— we shall not expect them to be just like us. There will always be a sense in which our earth is unique just as each one of us is unique. In their own way these other individuals may be as valuable to God as we. But the value of the one will not detract from the value of the other.

But Christians will be puzzled. Has Christ visited the galaxies in turn—suffering and dying now here, now there, for the sins of man-like creatures to reconcile them to God? We need not suppose it. Maybe God has planned other ways and means—each ideally suited for those He wishes to redeem.

Well, then, *are* there other beings? The question is difficult to discuss. On the one hand we may argue that a planet such as ours might be a rare occurrence if it arose as a result of chance. But *did* it come into existence by chance? In a universe so full of evidence for Plan, may not inhabited planets, too, have been planned? May there not have been direct intervention in the physical processes which brought them into existence? And, if so, science can tell us nothing about the frequency of intervention. Inhabited planets may exist in great numbers, or the numbers may be small or there may be but one.

Perhaps chemistry will give us a hint at this juncture. We have noted the remarkable way in which the elements fulfil the needs of life. This fact alone may convince us that they must play their role in a million galaxies. If God had only wished to create life here, would it not have been simpler to make a special sort of matter for our benefit alone—perhaps filling the rest of the universe with matter of a different kind? Yet the argument is dangerous for God's prodigality is such that He may not choose the way which to us seems the simpler.

Another possible line of speculation is mathematical. We count by adding. We even suppose that this is the natural way to count. Yet there is much evidence that it is not. If we may judge by nature, God counts not arithmetically but logarithmically. And, willy nilly, we often find that we, too, have to count and measure logarithmically, for otherwise we find our operations unbelievably cumbersome. Thus we have the *decibel* scale of sound intensity, a logarithmic scale of *magnitude* for the brightness of stars and we measure acidity and oxidizing power by such scales as pH and rH. In a thousand instances the simple laws of nature only reveal themselves when we count and measure logarithmically.

But when we think along these lines the sheer vastness of the universe disappears. We find to our surprise that the size of the earth, judged by the number of atoms it contains, is just about half-way between that of the atom and that of the entire observable universe, while we ourselves are more than a third-way up the scale. The proportion seems reasonable enough and there are the soundest scientific grounds for thinking that this viewpoint represents a natural, undistorted, mode of thought. And if so, it is fallacious to think of ourselves and our planet as a dot in space, trivial and insignificant. In any case, as we have already seen, chemistry reveals that, considered from the molecular point of view, we are vast indeed, incomparably more complex than stars and galaxies; great cosmic structures filled with an unimaginable maze of co-ordinated machinery.

And the purpose of existence? Again we trespass beyond the ken of science. But the religious instinct seems to tell us that, somehow, somewhere, man has a role to fulfil in the great cosmic process. Now we see darkly, but *then* face to face. "No eye has seen, nor ear heard, nor the heart of man conceived, what God has prepared for those who love Him," says St. Paul—apparently quoting the words of Jesus (the passage is found in the Gospel of Thomas). Expressions like "the riches of His glorious inheritance", "the riches of His glory", "His riches in glory", often occur in the New Testament, together with repeated hints that the glory will one day be shared by those who love God. It is a staggering conception. Will God's servants serve Him in distant worlds in the aeons to come, will they use their minds to implant ever more abundantly in the cosmos those evidences of Plan which we have discerned so repeatedly, will they perhaps help to formulate new strategies to bring fallen creatures back to God? Who shall say? But this we know—that science brings us a vista of unending grandeur and wonder, a sense of the unfathomable riches of God, which was denied to former generations.

INDEX OF NAMES

Agricola, 53
Albert of Saxony, 156
Alexander, J., 126, 189
Aquinas, 16, 45, 155, 197
Arago, M., 95
Aristotle, 18, 44, 45, 154, 197
Armstrong, H. E., 10
Arrhenius, S., 50, 68

Bacon, R., 156
Baldwin, J. L., 139
Ball, R. [Sir], 50
Ballard, F., 203
Barcroft, J. [Sir], 217
Barnes, E. W. [Bp], 164
Bastian, H. C., 121
Bell, C. [Sir],119
Bernal, J. D., 126, 134
Beutner, B., 126
Blum, H. F., 27, 104
Boltzmann, L., 21, 22
Born, M., 185
Bondi, H., 36
Boyle, R., 146
Brabazon, [Lord], 148
Brewster, D.[Sir], 19, 51
Bridgman, P. W., 34, 35, 198
Briggs, M. H., 83
Browne, Thomas [Sir], 200
Bruno, G., 46
Buffon, Comte de, 81
Burton, R., 48
Butler, J. A. V., 170

Chamberlin, R. T., 128
Chambers, R., 122
Cicero, 154, 194
Clark, R. E. D., 12, 31, 162
Collingwood, R. G., 177
Comenius, J. A., 224
Comte, A., 168
Copernicus, 46
Crick, F. H. C., 111
Crosse, A., 121
Culmann, 145
Curie, Madame & P., 10, 23
Daniel, 222
Darwin, C., 119, 122, 124, 126, 160, 161, 189
Davy, M. J., 143

Democritus, 44
Dingle, H., 21
Dixon, M., 134
Drake, 71
Duffy, B. J., 179
Duhem, P., 156
Dunbar, H. F., 177

Eddington, A. [Sir], 29 ff., 33, 34, 189
Einstein, A., 152, 167
Elizabeth 1, 46
Epictetus, 154

Fabre, 124
Flammarion, N. C., 50
Fort, C. H., 62
Fox, S. W., 126

Galen, 155
Galileo, 46, 47, 125
Gamow, G., 39
Gaudin, M., 94
Glagett, M., 18
Goethe, 160
Goldschmidt, V. M., 89, 128
Gordon, R. G., 189
Grant, R. M., 17
Gray, J. [Sir], 138, 139

Haeckel, E., 160
Haldane, J. B. S., 32, 127, 203
Haller, W., 157
Hardy, D., 215
Harris, R. J. C., 127
Harrison, E. R., 91
Hartill, I., 12
Hartung, E. J., 104
Harvey, Wm., 146, 166
Helmholtz, H. L. F. von, 120
Henderson, L. J., 97, 104, 163, 165
Herschel, J. [Sir], 49
Herschel, Wm. [Sir], 62
Hinshelwood, C. [Sir], 105
Hitler, 195
Hodgkin, D. C., 117
Hooke, R., 20
Horowitz, N. H., 126, 127
Hume, D., 186
Hunter, D., 147
Huxley, A., 193

Huxley, J. S., 41, 189
Huxley, T. H., 160
Huygens, C., 48

Jacks, G. V., 212
Jeans, J. [Sir], 67, 68, 81, 227
Jeffreys, H. [Sir], 84, 89
Jennison, G., 212
Job of Edessa, 155, 156
Jones, F. W., 162
Jones, H. S. [Sir], 67
Jones, W. H. S., 44, 211

Kant, I., 80, 192
Kekulé, F. A., 166
Kelvin [Lord], 11, 25
Kendrew, J. C., 137
Kepler, J., 48, 185
Keston, H., 46
Kuiper, G. P., 83, 85, 128

Lack, D., 97
Laird, J., 169
Langton, S. [A-bp], 157
Lankester, R., 50
Laplace, 80
Leduc, S., 121
Leibnitz, 179
Lemaître, 40
Leonardo da Vinci, 143
Levinthal, W. M., 207
Lewis, C. S., 195
Lovell, A. C. B., 85
Lowell, P., 69
Lucretius, 168
Lunn, A., 203
Luther, M., 46
Lyot, 68
Lyttleton, R. A., 81
McCabe, J., 29
Mach, E., 184
McColley, G., 48
Malthus, T. R., 161
Marais, E. N., 213
Markham, V., 145
Marliani, G., 18
Mascall, E. L., 30
Mason, I., 115
Maupertuis, 71, 185
Maxwell, J. C., 25, 225
Metrodorus, 44
Miller, S., 128
Milne, E. A., 29
Moffett, 53

Molyneux, W., 53
Montagu, M. F. A., 143
Moody, R. L., 208
Moorehead, McC., 212
More, H., 12
Mottram, V. H., 139
Mudd, S., 138

Neckam, A., 156
Needham, J., 29, 160
Newton, I. [Sir], 11, 19, 21, 24, 39, 150, 158

Oparin, A. I., 35, 126, 127, 128, 140
Opik, E. J., 35
Owen, R. [Sir], 140

Paley, W., 119, 158, 160
Pantin, C. F. A., 97, 104, 139
Paracelsus, 182
Pasteur, L., 121, 207
Paul, St., 154
Pauling, L., 107
Paxton, J., 144
Perutz, 111, 137
Pickering, W. H., 62
Plato, 44, 98
Pliny, 154, 155
Pope, A., 141
Praz, M., 161
Preston, J., 157
Preston, R. D., 146
Price, H., 34
Prochnow, 143
Proctor, R. A., 50

Raven, C. E., 164
Ray, J., 48
Reade, W., 193
Réaumur, R., 147
Romanes, G. J., 160, 217
Rosenberg, 195
Rubey, W. W., 128
Russell, B. [Earl], 29, 81, 189
Russell, E. S., 170
Rutherford, [Lord], 10, 13
Ryle, M., 37

Sanger, F., 137
Sarton, G., 143
Schaffer, J., 147
Schmidt, O., 83, 85
Schroedinger, E., 184, 185
Sciama, D. W., 184
Shaw, B., 205
Sherrington, C. [Sir], 120, 138, 189, 220 ff.
Sidgwick, N. V., 97, 104
Smalley, B., 157
Smith, H., 49
Solmsen, F., 15
Spencer, H., 37, 50
Stephens, E. J., 144
Sullivan, J. W. N., 21
Swedenborg, I., 49, 80
Swinton, W. E., 126
Teilhard de Chardin, 41, 189
Temperley, H. N. V., 218
Tennant, F. R., 198

Thomson, D'A., 122, 146
Thomson, G. P. [Sir], 144
Todd, A. [Sir], 117

Ubbelohde, A. R. J. P., 134
Urey, H. C., 83, 85, 127, 128

Van der Waals, 93

Waddington, C. H., 170
Wallace, A. R., 51
Ward, H., 120
Watson, J. D., 111
Webb, E. C., 134
Wellbye, R. F. D., 189
Werner, A. G., 160
Werner, A., 116
Westaway, F. W., 194
Wheeler, L. R., 162, 217
Whewell, Wm., 50
White, J., 212
Whittaker, E. T., 16, 155, 197
Whyte, L. L., 23
Whyte, R. O., 212
Wildt, R., 128
Wilkins, J. [Bp], 48
Wilson, R. McN., 216
Wolff, H. G., 215
Woolfson, M. M., 86, 91

Zinsser, H., 212
Zuelzer, 206

INDEX OF SUBJECTS

Adynata, 17
Ammonia, 63
Anatomy, Critics of, 203 ff.
Animals, Cruelty to, 212; Metallic, 95, etc.
Animism, Scientific, 181
Anthropomorphism, 182 ff.
Anti-matter, 54
Antiperistalsis, 18, 26
Anti-vitamins, 130
Arginine, 124
Asteroids, 71
Atmosphere, Earth's, 77, 105; of Planets, 63 ff., 77, etc.
Atoms, 167 ff., 180
ATP, 135

Baboons, 213; Limerick, 32
Bacillus Coli, 207
Bacteria, 52
Bats, 148
Bestiaries, 156
Birds, 170
Blood, 114, 147, 166, 185
Body, 204, 232; Mind on, 171; Wisdom of, 130
Bombs, Nuclear, 54
Bones, 143 ff.
Brain, 174
Bridgewater treatises, 158

Caddis-fly larvae, 170
Calcium, 113
Caloric, 20
Camera, 130
Camouflage, 148
Carbon, 96 ff., 106, 112
Carbon dioxide, 99, 114, 124
Carbon monoxide, 111
Carbonic anhydrase, 114
Cell, 135 ff.
Cellulose, 146
Chance, 21 ff.; Winding of Universe, 32 ff., 35
Charcoal, 89
Chemical, gardens, 121
Chemistry, 54, 190, 226, etc.; in Education, 117 ff.; Nature's copied, 149 ff.; Possibility

denied, 168
Chlorophyll, 113
Christianity, Astronomy and, 45 ff.
Chromosomes, 110, 135
Clouds, 75, 107
Cobalt, 116
Cold, 217
Comets, 71
Continents, 87
Counting, 235
Covalency, 95 ff.
Cow, 157
Creation, 15 ff., 176; Before, 37 ff., 194; Date of, 40; Continuous, 36 ff., 40; Importance of, 41 ff.; Newton on, 19
Cruelty, Nature's, 214 ff.
Crystal Palace, 144
Crystals, 26, 31, 94
Cucumbers, 155
Cycles, 14 ff., 35 ff.

Death, 216 ff.
Definitions, 192
Demiurge, 15, 16, 98 ff.
Demon, Maxwell's, 25, 225
Design argument, Critics of, 181 ff.; History of, 152 ff.; in Nature, 151
Devil, 201, 202
Disabilities, 203
Disease, Origin of, 206 ff.
Dogfish, 154
Dolphin, 150
Drugs, 150

Earth, Features of, 90, 156; Origin, 86 ff.; Small size, 48; Temperature, 103
Education, 117, 189
Egg, 22; Cooking of, 59
Electricity, 205
Elements, 105 ff.; Origin of, 38, 39
Energy, 11; Activation, 19; Chemical, 100; Free, 132 ff.
Engineering, 143 ff.
Entropy, 19 ff., 26 ff.
Enzymes, 107, 114, 124, 149
Erosion, 212

Evil, 159 ff., 200 ff., 230
Evolution, 33, 35, 41 ff., 83, 119, 123 ff., 179, 184 ff., 190
Exceptions, 8 ff.
Explanation, 182 ff.
Existence, 172
Eye, 120, 122, 150

Faculty psychology, 182
Films in reverse, 22
Firefly, 53
Fleas, Analogy of, 17, 59
Flight, 143
Fluorine, 112
Fly, Common, 151
Flying saucers, 83

Gaps, 9 ff.
Genes, 135 ff.; Linkage of, 125
Glass, 146
Glucose, 132 ff.
God, Gap theory, 9 ff.; Goodness of, 228; Impersonal theory, 193; Jesus and, 231 ff.; Nature of, 197; Personality in, 196; Who made?, 175
Granite, 87
Gravity, 184
Greeks, 43
Gyrotron, 151

Halieres, 151
Heat, 17 ff.
Heredity and learning, 170
Humility, 194, 229
Hydrogen, 106
Hypnosis, 177

Immunology, 107, 130 ff., 209
Impersonal Force, 193 ff.
Inertia, 184
Infinite Universe, 29
Infinity, 198
Instinct, 169 ff.
Instruments, 150
Insulin, 137
Inventions, 141 ff.
Invisible World, 167 ff.
Iodine, 115
Iron, 155, 156; Salts, 66; Ores, 89

Jesus, Teachings of, 231
Jupiter, 63

Laws of nature, 17
Learning, 170
Lens, 150
Lice, 159
Life, Chemistry of, 92 ff.; Elsewhere?, 52 ff., 233; Rarity, 72; Requirements of, 55, 73 ff., 78; Spontaneous generation of, 129, 133 ff.
Lions' den, 222
Logarithms, 235
Loneliness, Man's, 221
Lubrication, 149

Magnesium, 113
Magnetism, 173, 224
Malaria, 160, 211
Man, Vastness of, 236 Smallness, 235
Mars, 51, 65 ff.; Martians, 49
Mass, 184, 194
Materialism, 171 ff., 219 ff.
Mathematics, 184, 191, 227
Matter, Celestial, 53, 197
Mercury (metal), 204
Mercury (planet), 71
Metals, 95
Meteorites, 121
Methane, 63
Mind, 172, 229; Action on matter, 177; Cosmic, 192 ff., 229; in Nature, 163 ff.
Microscopes, 167
Miracles, 11; Hard to prove, 222
Modulation, 148
Mole, 146
Moon, 49 ff., 61, 62, 69, 86 ff.
Morpholysis, Law of, 23
Motor-car, 103, 204
Myoglobin, 137

Naturalism, 219 ff.
Natural Evils, 202 ff.
Natural Selection, 122 ff., 205 ff.
Nature, 181, 195; First inventor, 141 ff.; Cruelty of, 214 ff.; Unity of, 187 ff.
Neptune, 63

Neurospora, 124
New York Sun, 50
Nitrogen, 108 ff.
No-theories, 195
Nuclei (rain), 75
Nucleic acid, 110 ff., 134

Ocean, 86 ff., (See also Water)
Order, 21 ff., 163 ff. of Nature, 230
Organization, 55
Oxygen, 105 ff., 128, 149; Mars, 67
Ozone, 105

Pacific Ocean, 77, 87, 91
Pain, 215
Paper, 147
Paracrinkle, 206
Personality, 196 ff.
Philosophies, Two, 219 ff.
Phosphorus, 115 ff., 135
Photosynthesis, 103
Physics, 166
Planets, Origin of, 80 ff.
Plants, 101, 143
Poisons, 76, 89, 130, 174
Positivism, 165 ff.
Pride, 194, 229
Proteins, 137
Proto-planets, 83
Protoplasm, 120
Providence, 154, 159
Pyrrole, 113
Pythagorians, 44
Puritans, 157

Questions, 177 ff.

Radar, 148
Radioactivity, 10 ff., 100
Radio waves, 61, 62, 69, 71
Rain, 75
Reactions, 58, 101 ff.
Regress, 175
Relativity, 179
Reversibility, 16 ff.
Rivers, 17, 205
Romantics, 161
Russian astronomy, 82, 83, 85

Salt, 75, 89, 93
Saturn, 51, 63
Science, Philosophy of, 228; Scientific method, 3; Sinful to ignore, 157; Trend of, 90, 187; Truth and, 166

Sea, 76
Second law of thermodynamics, 20 ff.
Selectiveness, 234
Sermon on Mount, 231 ff.
Silicon, 97
Sin, 213
Size, 125 ff.; of Planets, 62 ff.; of Universe, 235
Sky-hook, 148
Smell, 150
Soil, 108
Solvents, 102
Specialization, 189 ff., 223
Spontaneous generation, 121
Stars, 56, 168
Struggle, 205 ff.
Sulphur, 76
Supernatural, 199

Tapeworm, 160, 208
Teapot analogy, 94, 95
Teeth, 112
Temperature, 55 ff., 58 ff.; of Earth, 102
Thyroxine, 115
Toxicology, 130 ff., 209
Tom-tit, 170
Truth, 166; Hidden from the wise, 18

Uniformitarianism, 160
Unity of Nature, 187 ff.
Universe, Age of, 40
Unobservables, 167 ff.

Vagueness, 164
Venus, 69 ff.
Viruses, 206
Vitamins, 207; B_{12}, 117
Volcanoes, 88

War, 211 ff., 215
Wasps, 147
Waste, 233
Water, 12, 65, 74, 101, 107 ff., 190; in Rocks, 78
"Winding" of Universe, 32
Wing, Vulture's, 143
Wireless set analogy, 123
Wood, 146
Worlds, Other, 43 ff., 233 ff.